A TIME TO STAND

CANDICE GIBBONS

Trilogy Christian Publishers
A Wholly Owned Subsidary of Trinity Broadcasting Network
2442 Michelle Drive
Tustin, CA 92780

For information, address Trilogy Christian Publishing
Rights Department, 2442 Michelle Drive, Tustin, Ca 92780.
Trilogy Christian Publishing/ TBN and colophon are trademarks of Trinity Broadcasting Network.

For information about special discounts for bulk purchases, please contact Trilogy Christian Publishing.

Manufactured in the United States of America

10 9 8 7 6 5 4 3 2 1

Library of Congress Cataloging-in-Publication Data is available.

ISBN 978-1-68556-121-5 (Print Book)
ISBN 978-1-68556-122-2 (ebook)

To the girl who just moved

CONTENTS

AUTHOR'S NOTE

The real "OEH" holds a special place in my heart. In no way is this book meant to offend the people who inspired the characters, or to demean the existing school. The views expressed herein are those of a sixteen-year-old girl. The events are partly fictionalized and partly a composite of things that really happened. Names and descriptions have been altered. The experiences of the main character have been tweaked and adjusted for dramatic effect. But, on the whole, this book is an accurate memoir of my spiritual and emotional journey, even if the setting is somewhat stylized. On behalf of Carissa and everyone else at OEH, do enjoy this delicious story.

Previously in A Time to Trust

I was standing in a school hallway that held the eerie feeling of being completely unrelated to anything past or present. It was a vision, and it would come true in less than six months.

"God is calling some of you to step out of your comfort zones into a great adventure, and your obedience and sacrifice will lead to great blessings" the pastor said. I assumed it was a feel-good statement. Then followed an awed silence over our family as we realized "change" was coming. It was too wrong to be true. I tried to rationalize the situation and convince myself that it was just my own brain pretending to be God. Yet He was speaking to me that *we* were the family about to step out of our comfort zone. I did not want this change to happen, but I knew that it must.

It was the first of several distinct prophecies. God asked me to trust Him with my life—more specifically, with my future. What did that even mean? I asked Him to help me understand. At the same time, I hoped nothing would change, that my comfortable home and family would sail seamlessly ahead. And, in the worst case, if there had to be change, maybe it would only *semi*-affect me. Like, maybe we would paint our yellow cottage blue, or something to that extreme.

My dad told us to start praying about moving to another state. That was not possible. The Von Trapp family moved. Riley Andersen moved. *Random kids in movies moved*—not Candice. Yet, soon enough, pieces started fitting together. Before I could reverse the vision and reverse the prophecies, Mom and Dad announced we were moving to Oklahoma.

A red FOR SALE sign was hammered in our pretty green lawn. Cardboard boxes popped up and were packed. People hugged us and cried. My parents did all the typical stuff people do when they move, like renting U-Hauls. I accepted it. It was not one big *ah-ha* moment. I was less like sweet, trusting Mary and more like stoic Job, who technically had no alternative option. And, just as Job faced his trials, I turned my head westward for Oklahoma, not knowing what it all meant, or what I was supposed to do, or why any of it mattered.

I am moving to a state known for cowboys and thunderstorms. I have been accepted into a prestigious private school by the name of Oklahoma Excellence. I am on pins and needles to start my new life as a sixteen-year-old private schooler, and I am determined to live for Christ for the rest of my life. And this is where the story picks up.

"The Lord had said to Abram, "Leave your native country, your relatives, and your father's family, and go to the land that I will show you. I will make you into a great nation. I will bless you and make you famous, and you will be a blessing to others."
Genesis 12:1-2 (NLT)

Chapter 1

VITA NOVA

January 4ᵗʰ

F IVE SECONDS AGO, childhood ended. Its conclusion was anticlimactic. The car door did not slam, and my grandparents did not cry. No one was wearing black. The entire goodbye was a bit too casual. The motor vroom muffled what could have been ceremonial silence, and the wind was so deafening I barely heard the last words of my grandmother. Not that she was dying; I was. My entire life was dissolving like bubbles down a drain. I tried pushing my black tennis shoes against the floorboard as if I controlled the brakes, but that did not freeze our car from inching out of my grandparents' farm and away, away, away from childhood security.

Now, bits of sleet are stabbing the ground and fog is chalking the air, mirroring vague and undetectable thoughts in my mind. Winter's rotten grass and skeleton trees blend together like a beige palette. I squint at the horses lining the fence and wonder if I am going blind: the world looks like an expired salad. That's right, expired. My life here has expired. And maybe it is the product of salty tears mixing with mascara, or maybe I am actually losing my vision, but it appears a large tomato is gliding by as we approach and pass the red barn. We now near the fork-like iron gates that lead out of Riverview Ranch. Thinking of *ranch* makes me hungry.

The blinker clicks. We merge on the highway.

"Well, this is it," sighs Dad. "This. Is. It."

Yes, this *is* it. I am not even sure we will come back. I bet everyone in Ozark, Missouri, will forget about us. We will become one of those families mentioned from time to time like, "Remember the Gibbons family? Didn't they used to live here?" as if we did not carve our names in the cement at our yellow cottage. As if our cousins, aunts, uncles, and grandparents on both sides of the family did not live here. As if I was not in the best friend group imaginable, and literally just about every time I went to Walmart, I saw someone I knew.

"Bye, bye, Ozark." Waves my eight-year-old sister, Angel. Cuddled in her purple housecoat, her hair is bunched in unicorn sleep goggles masking her forehead. She is clutching two sparkly stuffed animals and smiling at her reflection. I turn to my refrigerator-glazed window and wave goodbye to every landmark I have passed on the backroads of Missouri for the last sixteen years. *Goodbye, old cemetery. Goodbye, rickety bridge. Goodbye, creepy two-story cabin with all of the random antiques in the front yard.* The sun should be rising, but it is too cloudy to notice. Just like my life: hopeless. This really is quite sad. Here we are, driving away from the only home I have ever known, and...

what sixteen-year-old gets to start her life over?

I am overanalyzing everything. This is rather exciting. Maybe that is why I am on the edge of this seat tapping my feet. Or maybe it is just cold. I like how it is cold. If it were warm and comfortable, I would be agitated. This moment should be uncomfortable, sobering. Whatever has happened before this point, and I mean *everything*, I have cut it into an entirely different section of my life: goodbye childhood. Yet even though it is sad to move away, it is an immensely wonderful opportunity. Moving: it is the beginning of a new *you*.

Here we are. Same seats. Different people. I feel like my identity was just burned. Buried and burned. Like, you never fully realize how much of your personality is nurtured by your surroundings until you are uprooted. Southern Missouri's barefoot nature, the aloofness of carefree children at the park, the tractors and cows and small-town diners, all of it has formed me to be a private, simple girl, one who wears boots and button-ups and braids, one who asked for a walking stick for her birthday and likes to play in creeks. But Oklahoma? The culture and people will clash with my heritage. They will think differently and dress differently. So, either I can grip to southern Missouri or allow myself to melt into a Missouri-Oklahoman. I must think about this.

We are now approximately 2 ½ hours from our rental house. The highway route is vaguely familiar; we made two trips to Oklahoma last semester to deliver some of our furniture and tour our new school. It is called Oklahoma Excellence High school, and they do not capitalize the 's,' so it is called 'OEH.' For the first time I seriously sound it out in my head. *OEH. OEH. Oeh…oeh…oeh…* it sounds like a tribal chant. We are passing some Cherokee memorial landmarks right now. I think Oklahoma is the central spot for many Native American tribes. Do not ask me how I know this, wait until I take my course in Oklahoma History. I never took a Missouri History class. Maybe I was about to before I moved…

I am starting a game with myself to critique casino slogans on billboards. Ozark does not have any casino billboards nor any casinos. But here I go again comparing. There is no need to associate Oklahoma's red dirt with Missouri's rocky hills, because today marks the beginning of a new chapter in Candice Gibbons's life, not a repeat of the past. This is sixteen. This is my sophomore year. And the only element lacking in this moment is a soundtrack—a progressive, motivational, piano soundtrack with some drums and maybe a French horn thrown in.

Dad blows on his coffee. "What are you looking forward to the most?"

"Slamming a locker door. Juggling schoolbooks down the hall while talking to friends. It's what I have always imagined high school being like. Like a kid who goes to school every day. Like in the movies." In my eyelids I am swaggering in slow motion through the hall with popular girls at either side, hair blowing from the winds of football players' high-fives.

"School is not exactly like the movies."

"I'm mentally prepared." I assure him, inwardly disagreeing. I am a strong idealist.

"Have you thought about joining a club?"

"Like Track and Field?"

"That's considered a sport, not a club. What about something to do with film or writing?"

"I am already taking Journalism class," I remind him.

"Oh, Daddy, sign me up for theater!" Angel squeals.

"Drama is the last thing this family needs." Dad mutters.

"I know I am not an athlete, Dad. But Candice the homeschooler is joining a private school and moving to the city. Why *not* join track? I may even win a medal."

"Not every track runner has screws in her feet."

"I'm just saying, since our lives have practically flipped upside down, Candice plans to accomplish a lot this semester." I give a little grin and nod my head, as if it will make him nod, too.

Dad smiles. He has always encouraged me and my wild ideas, as long as they aren't permanently damaging. "Go win that medal."

So that is what I am going to picture: a gold, shiny medal with my name on it. After all, God promised me blessings if I moved here. I have high expectations. But how can I assure myself I am ready for track? Once I arrive in Oklahoma, it is go-time. As in, put on those spikey shoes runners wear and join the pack. Where do I even buy track shoes? And should I really consider joining a sport right off the bat? Maybe I should just slide in easy, making sure I can get to the right class at the right time, and slip in the open side of the desk. Let's put first things first, like learning how to get from class to class in under five minutes, understanding the homework system, joining a good lunch table. And once the waters are tested…

But I did not come here to play it safe.

My thoughts scatter. One moment, I am confident. The next moment, I am in survival mode, grasping at self-preservation. But I must remember I am here out of obedience, not for comfort. There is so much to consider about this pattern of change, and it seems worthy of constant thought. Obedience: moving. Sacrifice: well, everything—right down to our less-than-ideal rental house. Blessing: who knows? Based on what I have read, I just figure it follows sacrifice. I am living in stage two. I need to go all in.

I close my eyes and see my two, tall grandparents in the driveway of Riverview Ranch, still waving us off in bundled sweaters and coats, wishing us safe driving and no bad weather and to "watch out for those I-35 semitrucks." I said goodbye to my old room a long time ago. Like two whole days. That is why we left childhood from the launchpad of the farm. And now, I just want to unpack all these blue duct tape cardboard boxes marked CANDICE. It is time to establish my new self, my fearless, Oklahoma self.

And yes, I am going to become an Oklahoman.

The rental house: cold, gray, and absolutely splendid. The perfect tinder for school life. Sterile, bare, and naturally lit. Smells like chlorine. Reminds me of the hospital smell of OEH. The rest of my family, Mom, Kelly, Bria, Allison, and Jordan are close to arriving in Big Roy, Mom's black suburban that rattles loudly. The car mechanic said it is harmless, that it is some exterior problem with the dashboard. Big Roy is exceptionally spacious, but always crammed, like a garage or suitcase. Since the rest of my family is still bobbing down the highway to the rattle of Big Roy, it almost feels like we left them in Missouri. I consider naming the rental house but decide it would make me endeared; I don't plan on becoming friends. Mom and Dad assured me they are planning to rebuild our childhood cottage here in Missouri—*that* will be home. Suppose I play we are living in a hotel for a few months. Minus the pool.

Entering my bleak new room, the flashback reels roll: Mom playing her piano, Jordan and Angel riding scooters around the kitchen island's sparkly granite, preteens Bria and Allison belting out a love song, dishes clattering as Kelly bakes bread, and Charlie the chihuahua-yorkie barking at the mailman. Noise was normal in our creamy cottage with brown shutters, and every day was a tea party, mildew investigation, roly-poly hunt, or living room talent show.

But now I will be at a boring school all day. I hum the theme song from the movie *Up,* the sad part of the chorus alluding to time's illusion and death's inescapability. My old room was cobalt and draped with warm Christmas lights, with white curtains over two nearly floor-to-ceiling windows, a white dresser and a damask comforter on a bleached trundle bed. That same bed will soon be in this room, but it will not have the same aesthetic sensations. There is only one rectangular window in here, and it is smushed in the corner, overlooking the neighbors fence I could probably reach out and touch with my hand. I feel a bit paranoid.

I unzip my black suitcase and stare in disgust. The steely walls remind me of the western wind: chalky, staticky, parched. The good news is I have a few décor pieces from my old room, the bad news is, Kelly will be moving into this space with her pink and floral color scheme in just a matter of minutes. I don't know how we're going to make this work.

I hear a two-pitch dinging sound. It must be our new doorbell. Our old doorbell was a four-ring church bell melody, mimicking real church bells that echoed across the cow pasture behind our house. This one sounds like a piece of machinery, like an elevator button or a wheelchair-accessible door buzzer. It fits with this place feeling like a prison.

"Can you get that?" Dad calls from his room, but the house is so small, it sounds like he is standing at my door.

The doorbell rings again. Someone knocks five times, obviously enthusiastic.

I squeeze past towers of cardboard boxes. "Coming!"

"Surprise!" I am greeted by Pastor Jackson and his entire family. Everyone is beaming, loaded with gold balloons, two gallon of sweet tea, three boxes of chicken, and a decorated sign with the word WELCOME! in neon green bubble letters. Two families trail behind with more signs and bouquets of balloons.

Angel restrains Charlie, who thinks he is our Rottweiler. "Who are *they?*"

"Shhhh," I welcome the parade into the house. "Come in! Come in! *Dad…"*

He knew they were coming. He is standing in the living room videoing us. I cannot believe these people from New Life Church would come welcome us to Oklahoma. They are, in fact, the reason we are here. Dad is going on staff as one of the pastors at New Life's multi-cultural church. I feel honored and guilty at the same time. We aren't *that* special.

"Hurry up and hide," a random girl pulls my arm. We crouch below the counter.

"Hello! What is your—"

"Tia Samone. Our dads work together now," she whispers.

"Really?"

"Shhh!"

These strangers are helping themselves to hiding places high and low. Is it their house? Is it my house? Frankly, I could not care less. There is no such thing as normal. I scan the kitchen trying to familiarize myself with everyone's faces. The families are multi-racial, and many are wearing Oklahoma sports gear. I feel like an intrusive blueberry in my oversized navy sweatshirt and freckled face of cluelessness to social cues. *Forget yourself,* I say, but it does not work.

"Hey, hey, hey, here is the rest of their family—everyone *shh!* Three, two, one… *Surprise!"*

My mom, along with my four sisters and little brother, are standing dumbstruck in the doorway, completely caught off guard. Seeing my golden sister Kelly's appearance makes me wish I had dressed up. But again, I did not know this was going to be a party. Our new church family is so welcoming, so hospitable, and so intriguing. This reminds me of Thanksgiving, except I am at someone else's family reunion…underdressed.

"You're from Missouri, right? Haha, kind of sounds like 'misery.' It wasn't miserable, was it? Did you like it there, or were you ready to move? I mean like, was it a good change? Did you leave a boyfriend or something? *I* sure did…" Tia rambles. She has tiny black braids and is sporting a Cross Country sweatshirt. She is a *real* runner.

"Oh, really?" I feel inferior.

"We moved here from Boston last summer. Quite the change, moving south." She says in a nippy, northeastern accent. She is pouring a gallon jug of sweet tea into plastic cups, sipping the first one she makes. "Like this tea. It's so sweet!"

"Really?" I repeat, filling empty cups with ice cubes to feel less awkward. "We moved here from Missouri. It wasn't miserable." The coldness is jarring. I start to think about how cold it must be in Boston in the wintertime and shiver. I bet they drink nasty, unsweet tea, too. "Anyways, so, you're from Massachus—"

"Right-o, spaghettio." She grins a glaring set of neon green braces. Minus the braces, she looks a twinge older than me. I smile back. Maybe we will be friends.

Curled hair and diamond-necklaced Kelly is walking towards us. "Hello, Tia. I remember meeting you when our dad spoke here in October of last year. Candice, Tia is a senior, you know." She says like I am supposed to be impressed. I am.

"I heard you guys are starting OEH!" Interjects Jeremiah Jackson, second oldest of the Jackson siblings. "Very cool!"

"Yes, yes I am very excited," Kelly smiles at him.

"As you should be. On Monday you'll have to do community service. Each grade will be sent to some city outreach. We always start the semester with community service. It is, in my opinion, much needed for the student body." He nods his head matter-of-factly.

Kelly and Jeremiah start to talk about Pre-AP Classes and end up on a theological rabbit trail about what we will do for eternity, but my mind has immediately shifted to the den of lions awaiting me—a den of blond-haired, fake eyelash-wearing princesses scheming out my arrival. I try to imagine Carissa Carlyle—*the* queen of OEH—picking up trash or power washing a sidewalk, but I just can't see it. I start to laugh, and everyone stares at me.

"Isn't moving *scary?*" Tia lifts the awkwardness.

I widen my eyes, but before I launch into my life story complete with graphic mouth surgery details from last summer, I remind myself, *enough overdramatization. You are going to be okay.* Since I am emotional today, I simply nod, unsure of what will come out of my mouth. Tia leaves to talk with Bria and Allison. Amidst blurry

8

eyes I see everyone is exchanging hugs and tying balloons to barstool crowns. Like family.

After everyone eats and mingles, Pastor Jackson gathers the crowd to pray.

"Heavenly Father, thank you for blessing us with the Gibbons family. I pray for special protection and anointing on their lives in this new season. May they find joy from trusting You by moving here, and may they feel at home in Oklahoma City. Amen."

And just like that, something clicks. Not everything, but something. Whether it is Tia's firm grip on my shoulder, Pastor Jackson's prayer, or the familiar steam of fried chicken, I feel accepted and energized. This is new life, literally and figuratively. This is not the last puzzle piece of my life; this is the first click of a new landscape. It may not be home, but I already love this community. And I don't know whether to label it 'adulthood' just yet, but this is certainly not warm, fuzzy childhood.

This is the Oklahoma. This is sixteen. This is my sophomore year.

Chapter 2

COMMUNITY SERVICE

KELLY'S NOSE CONTORTS at my gray sweatshirt like I am wrong for dressing casual.

"It's community service day—as in *work*—remember?"

"I suppose. But I am still wearing a sweater. It makes me feel smart. You can have first shift in the bathroom."

"Gracias," I skip off.

The door is locked.

"I'm in here," says Bria groggily. She is newly thirteen.

Kelly and I had our own bathroom in Missouri. It was a jack-and-jill bathroom with cerulean walls and rubber ducky towels and plush banana rugs. Aside from a spider problem, it was comfortable and ideal. But now, even the ducky bathroom is gone. The grass is always greener... "How long will you be?"

"Leaving in five minutes!" Mom yells.

"Never mind; enjoy." I tell Bria, walking three steps back and five steps to the right into the main quarter of the house, my Plan B spot for getting ready, which may very well become Plan A for the rest of my life. This space serves as the living room, kitchen and dining room, and now, Candice's vanity mirror. Our familiar square glass is propped against the wall, and if I suck in my stomach and squeeze my eyes, I can fit between it and the dining room chairs. I smile at my reflection out of convincement, unweaving my French braids that barely survived the night. I pin back two chunks with bobby pins and stare at my ever so evolving sixteen-year-old self in the mirror. I never knew moving would be such an opportunity to start fresh.

Before I have time to think deep thoughts, we are arriving at Oklahoma Excellence High school: *my* school.

"You are loved by God, gifted for greatness, and never alone… because God is with you," Mom's voice deflates. It is the statement she has declared over us since preschool. But she is exhausted—not the kind of exhaustion a night's sleep can fix, exhaustion from days of stress and the grind of responsibility. Poor Mom. Kelly and I hug her, thanking her for being our teacher for all these years and all that. Old life dying; new life beginning.

Thank you, Mom, for a secure childhood.

Kelly walks ahead of me. She seems eager to begin her first day. She knows where her class is. I am having second thoughts. Am I really ready to step into this new world? I can't think about it. I have to figure out where I am going. Look confident…look confident…"Mrs. Gray?" It feels like an eternity before the administrative receptionist peers over her wiry glasses. The school's hand sanitizer smell is killing every confident bone in my body.

"Like it said in the email you received, go to the sophomore Bible class on the third floor, Room 302. Next," she motions to an acne-stricken boy with cut off sleeves, too short shorts, and cowboy boots waiting behind me. He is built like a wrestler.

I guess emails matter. "Ma'am, where are the stair—"

"Oh, hello, Candice. I'll show you." Principal Vanderbilt enters in exceptional timing. She is wearing a strawberry pencil dress, chocolate hair in a pastry bun. I walk two paces behind her out of respect. We pass Kelly in a freshman classroom, who has probably already found her new friend circle. A group of girls are complimenting the very sweater I told her not to wear. She doesn't see me. Maybe they're laughing at me in my casual sweatshirt. I bet they are planning a sleepover at a rich girl's house, where they will giggle and paint nails and become besties for life while I sit at home and count blades of dead grass.

Principal Vanderbilt is informing me how exciting this day is going to be while I am absent-minded. Behind me I spot Isabelle and Mabrey, two girls I met on my shadow day, a few feet behind us on the staircase. Odds are, they are going to the same classroom as I am, so I should smile and make eye contact. Even if they are not my first picks for friends, at least I can establish myself on friendly terms. When you are the new kid—and I am—you just can't pretend to understand social dynamics—it is too risky. You really don't know assets from liabilities.

All the same, curly-headed Isabelle smiles back spitefully and Mabrey just scowls. I hear them whisper about how I ate at the "popular table" with Carissa Carlyle. Of course, that was only because I was Carissa's shadow student. I *had* to sit with her. But I guess I am already labeled as a cheerleader. Speaking of cheerleaders, I have not seen a single member since I've been here—not Carissa or Callie or anyone else who sat at the lunch table on my shadow day. Are they planning to make some kind of big entrance?

"…that is why half the school isn't here." I catch the last part of Principal Vanderbilt's words. "Students are given the option to go on a mission's trip during Christmas break and skip community service."

Now I know exactly where the popular kids are, which makes sense when we enter a science classroom, and I am greeted by a pair of wide-rimmed glasses and short purple pigtails. Illustrated posters of deoxyribonucleic acid with eyes and eyebrows are plastered around us. The whiteboard wall is white; the enclosing walls are red like blood. The room *smells* like blood. No; it smells like the alcohol wipes applied before the nurse draws blood. There is a large U-shaped table in the center of the classroom occupied by a supply of regularly awkward sophomores—nerdy, hairy, gothic, and yet remarkably stuck up. Some of them look older than me, like college aged. And this girl, in particular, is definitely *not* your OEH popular girl stereotype.

"Have a blessed day." Principle Vanderbilt—my only hope—leaves. *Au revoir.*

Purple pigtail girl seizes her opportunity. "Never seen your face before."

"Hello, my name is Candice," I smile grittily. If talking to her isn't a strike to my social circle and chances of becoming popular, I don't know what is.

"Candice...Candice..." she snaps her fingers like she's trying to remember something.

"Oh, *you're* that girl everyone's talking about."

"Really?" I have a nervous habit of speaking in adverbs under stress.

"You're the biggest thing that's happened to the sophomore grade since Isaac Kennedy got temporarily suspended last semester for coming to school high. 'Course, he wasn't the first."

"Oh?"

"And he's back now, by the way. There he is. The one with the cowboy boots."

"Really?"

"Get used to it. You *think* this is a good, Christian school, but wait 'til you come to a party. I'm Keli, and I'm a party in of itself."

I subdue a laugh and we shake hands. She is awfully friendly— the only student half interested in me. I note her eccentric crossbody purse decorated with bottle pins and hair clips while deciding what to ask next, but I am caught off guard by another girl theatrically flinging herself in the classroom.

"I *barely* made it!" Every conversation halts. "Thanks to Mountain Smoothie's long line," she slurps her pink drink plucked with a polka-dotted straw. "Rush hour."

"That's Frida. She's Hispanic."

"Oh,"

"What ethnicity are you?"

I cough uncomfortably.

"Heck, I don't know what I am. *But I do know what he is!*" She winks at a boy with a mustache who pretends to shoot a gun at us from the other leg of the U-shaped table.

I don't want to know what she means or why she is on this topic, so I clear my throat and open my mouth to redirect, only to hear another voice come out—a voice of a teacher: *"Students sign the roster by the door and divide into buses and cars."*

Keli eyes me desperately. "Look, I don't have any friends here."

"What about that bo-…"

"Wanna to sit together?"

What would Carissa think? I think. *No, that's not a good question. What would Jesus do?*

So, I squish into the backseat of English teacher Mrs. Abernathy's Volkswagen with Keli, separated by Mrs. Abernathy's infant son's car seat. Mabrey is in the front seat, but I would not have noticed without looking. She is slumped over and has not said a word on the whole trip. But even moody Mabrey seems like a step up from purple-hair Keli, who smells a bit dangerous now that I think about it. I can't believe I am stuck with *these* girls after networking with all the popular kids I was introduced to during my shadow day in December. Part of me wants to brag about how I already know people and I am not desperate for anyone's help. I want to explain how I've sort of already been invited to the popular circle, how Carissa actually offered for me to join cheer, and that I am not interested in becoming a member of the Goth Girl's Club.

I need to be like Jesus. Why does it seem so hard? Maybe this is the beginning of the sacrifice chapter. Like, not walking down a hallway with my hair blowing in the wind. Because that is *so* not the case. Dad was right about school not being like the movies.

"So, Kansas, what are your interests?" Mrs. Abernathy is kind enough to break the tension.

"It's *Candice*," Keli corrects. "Like Candace off *Phineas and Ferb*."

"My apologies," Mrs. Abernathy nods in the rearview mirror, *"Candice."*

I smile understandingly, opening my mouth to engage in small talk. I can tell by Mrs. Abernathy's jacket, water bottle, and keychain that she coaches tennis, so I aim to mention something athletic. Not that I am an athlete. "Well, I had foot surgery in eighth grade. They broke both of my feet and repositioned the bones with screws. I had to stop dance, which was my thing. I am thinking about trying out for track.

But I am not a runner. Er, I mean, I am not an athlete." I sound like a complete fool—to myself, and probably even worse to everyone else.

Keli laughs. "Who runs with broken feet?"

"They're not broken any—"

"You're insane." Keli interrupts. "But aren't we all?" She laughs, and then pauses for a moment as if she is contemplating something deep. "Heyyy, you could always join the lame art club with Mabrey."

A coughed-issued silence follows. Noting Mrs. Abernathy's rainbow steering wheel cover with the word ART repeated over and over, the comment must directly affect her, too.

You would think a car ride with the awkward girls would be a breeze, given these girls might think I am prettier, taller, smarter, etc. But seriously, none of those qualities matter. I am new. I am on the outside looking in. And I am feeling more inferior by the second. Knowledge really does outweigh strength.

I turn to the window and fidget with my blue string bracelet. Why can't I think of something to say? In an attempt to escape this situation and prepare for school, I try to play out every scenario: like, what to say if Carissa spills coffee on my cream sweater, what to do if Mr. Groath calls me to the white board to do trigonometry. You have to plan for the worst.

We are honking through Oklahoma City's 9:00 a.m. traffic, and I am amazed to see so many luxury cars at once: a Tesla on our bumper, a Lamborghini to the right, and a car I have never even seen before in front of us. In Ozark, John Deer tractors are parked at stoplights. You might even see an Amish buggy on the side of the highway. But we are like an ant in a maze of waxed convertibles and reflective skyscrapers. Rap music hammering so loudly next to us makes our car vibrate. Keli dances to their music. Construction cranes crank overhead, and I clutch at my seatbelt. City life is so unfamiliar.

We pull up to an inner-city youth center marked by a line of green dumpsters. The place is embellished with graffiti and skateboard posters. Cobwebs and mildew give the paint an orange peel texture. It looks like a Sunday school classroom, minus Jonah and the flannel board. And thank goodness; last summer I felt like Jonah running away from God. It was a horrible feeling of wrongness. I shake off the chill of guilt.

I am all in with this. I am all in with this.

I hope we don't get shot.

The ceiling lights are low and dim. It's damp, too, like a laundry room. We are actually up a few stairs, but there seems to be a malfunction in the floorplan. This whole building cocks like a demo project. A bearded millennial wearing a flat bill hat shakes our hands and thanks us for coming. I feel a twinge of anger inside when I hear some older boys making fun of the smell of the room and the brown stains on the ceiling tiles.

You can't take volunteers for granted. Being a pastor's kid, I sense I should thank him for his "time and effort." I can almost feel my dad's hand on my back. I step out from our informal queue and thank the millennial for allowing *our school* to volunteer. I am still not sure what that means. Will we be scrubbing toilets? Interacting with inner-city kids? It feels weird to own OEH as my school, but it is the truth, no matter how inferior I feel.

"It means a lot that you guys came," the millennial screeches in a microphone. "Ugh, I guess you didn't have a choice. But man, what you're about to do can literally change lives. That's what we're all about here." He pounds his heart like a one-handed gorilla.

What exactly are *we about to do, give open heart surgeries?* I nod, hoping to appear interested. How difficult it must be to talk to a room full of disinterested rich kids. Give me a break. They need a wake-up call to reality.

What am I saying? *I* need a wake-up call. *I* am the one stuck in my own head.

"I know it can be hard to relate, since you guys have had everything handed to you in life," he strains, "but man, this center means the world for kids who don't have anywhere to go after school. Being honest with you guys, I used to be one of those kids." His words are followed by such a thick, dry silence, you could cut it.

A few teachers clear their throats. I want to tell the disheartened millennial to save face and just stop talking, but he feels the need to say more.

"You see, I was shot in the head three times…" he removes his flat bill and exposes three ghastly scars with staples and stitches. Isaac Kennedy yawns inappropriately.

"I was a member of the OKC gang called the…well, anyways, it was a tough crowd. But Jesus came into my life, and He restored my brokenness. I found a church and a community, and now I am trying to help other inner-city youth get out of gang lifestyles."

"Wish he'd given me the name of his gang. I'll have to slip 'em a little something later." Keli whispers to me.

I shake my head 'no' with a disapproving smile, like a mom to her whining kid. I already feel a connection with her, like I have known her for years. She is oddly familiar in a creepy way. Like maybe I was supposed to come to OEH just for her. You know what else? I feel a connection with this guy. Not that I was ever in a gang, but like I am called to be a leader at my school, just as he is a leader with these inner-city kids.

The spiritual temperature of OEH is like milk toast—a Christianized milk toast. Most kids have spoken fluent Christianese their entire lives—me included. It is the language of networking, college admissions interviews, clubs, and societies. And I always wondered if I meant what I said. But I don't wonder anymore because I have stopped pretending to be a Christian. I *am* one. Not in the American title sense, but as someone who follows Christ. I don't play games; this isn't religion.

The millennial peels back the rusted door on a utility closet and I have a chance to find out if I mean what I say. It looks like an entire Lowe's store crammed into a floor-level bomb shelter. At first, we all just stare. The task looks impossibly tedious. Typical of my personality, I do not even want to touch this stuff. Let's trash it all. In fact, let's burn the closet. The whole building. Let's start over. But this is idealism, not realism. Life is messy and so is this closet: we must deal with it. To switch perspectives, I tell myself to picture a weary nine-to-fiver voluntarily helping out, searching for a screwdriver to tighten up a city kid's broken toy or to insert batteries for the video game console adjacent to this wall. We can do this much for them.

This all sounds great in my mind, but in reality, I simply walk away in denial to a cluster of boys turning on the console to have a round of whatever people play on video games. My feet are curving inward, one in front of the other. I stare at them for answers. *Poor, pushover Candice. If I can't lead a simple cleaning project, how can I lead an entire school?*

I turn around.

"Can you lift this hardware box?" I ask a big senior football player, rolling up the sleeves to my sweatshirt. I tell the students to take everything out and then instruct two kids to organize supplies into sections. Keli has abandoned me, floating around the room with her earbuds dangling from her head in search of the mustached guy. Curly-headed Isabelle won't stop complaining about her feet. I am tempted to yell back that mine hurt worse. The truth is my feet are on fire right now, even though I am even wearing comfortable tennis shoes. This is a bad sign. Maybe track isn't such a good idea.

"Break time," A teacher says.

I am surprised at how far we've come on the utility closet. It does not look half as bad as before. I even hear a couple kids talk about how it was kind of fun organizing all of the knickknacks into stacks. *That's right,* I smile reflectively, *it is fun helping others and doing something active. It gets your mind off yourself.* I roll down my sleeves and walk to the food line. It is strange: hard work really can replace the fuel of needing companionship and dispel feelings of awkwardness. It is like its own purpose. I am glad I finally stepped up, even if it was delayed.

"New girl." Isabelle hunches over me as I walk out of the line. "Sit with us."

Frankly, I was hoping for a chance to sit beside a group of quiet girls at one of the corner booths and make my first direct attempt to influence. "Sure." I agree. To my surprise, we walk over to the very booth of girls I was eyeing, and Isabelle introduces me to the circle. If this isn't a hit to my reputation...

"Y'know, Candice might try out for cheer," Isabelle blurts out. *How does she know that?*

"She shadowed *Carissa Carlyle*. So I'm trying to introduce her to some, er, more *civilized* company." She says as if she is doing me a favor. Then she takes my hand to a separate eating section where Keli and some equally alarmingly dressed sophomores lounge. And this is *private school* attire? Yes, it is. Some teens are in a corner, and I wish I could go break their little love party, especially because I am feeling rather bold and righteous at the moment. But I have got to keep my cool. I am still the new kid. I need to establish common ground.

"Some freshman stole my name!" Keli explodes.

"Who?" Mustache Boy demands in a deep voice. He sounds forty.

"I don't know who the…" she stops midsentence when I sit down. "Wait…don't you have a freshman sister?"

"Yeah," I stammer, "Her name is Kelly Grace."

"Her sister stole your name!!!"

"Don't worry, she goes by her full name, Kelly Grace. I am like the only one who calls her 'Kelly.'"

Keli mutters colorful words and sheepishly smiles. "Well, how could I have known it was her?" She bites off a chunk of pepperoni pizza. As if this conversation could not get more awkward, everyone goes onto talk about the latest relationship scandal within the student body that happened over Christmas break. I hear more than I care to remember. I really hope none of the teachers think I am becoming one of them. Keli has more allies than she cared to admit to me, and the man-boy, whose name is Kenny, is definitely part of a rough crowd—rougher than Isabelle and Mabrey. "Have you ever done drugs?" Keli leans over the table. She is pulling out a mini jar of neon green nail polish to touch up her eccentric appearance.

Partly for the fun of it, I want to make up some kind of extreme answer to shock the druggies. But, remembering how I am a light—a Christ-follower—I shake my head honestly.

"Well, if you ever need to know where the good stuff is…"

"Shut up, Keli. Don't put that kind of pressure on her." Says Isabelle.

"I'm just *sa-ying*…" Keli drags out with a smile.

"What she means is, if you ever need some…uh, *help*, her locker is 11-…" Kenny plays.

"Would you please *stop?*" The theatrical girl—Frida, I recall—yells across the room. "You have already ruined half of the sophomore class. Don't spoil the new girl on her first day!"

In an attempt not to be heard by a teacher, Keli winks and lowers her voice. "You should know that our grade is the *cliquiest*. As in, even the seniors are afraid of us. Especially me."

This is just great. Here I am thinking we could have been friends. I mean, she was so nice when we met. Then again, I should have read the signs.

"Have you ever kissed anyone?"

"Do you think anyone here is hot?"

"Would you go on a date with that guy over there?"

This lunch break is dragging on longer than I prefer. Boys and girls keep asking me these nonsensical questions like they matter. I regret to admit how many boys have tried to flirt with me and continue to fail miserably, which makes me half uncomfortable yet partly sorry for them. I mean, they are all like sixteen just trying to make it in the world like me.

"We like to have a fun with the newbies," Isabelle grins, joining the barstool table. "This is so rare. Hey, want to ride with us on the bus back?"

At this point, I am thankful for the offer. At least she doesn't smell like drugs.

Mrs. Abernathy lets us switch seating arrangements. Keli decides to take the bus, too, but not because of me. I am actually not sure why she joined us. It is freezing in this bus, and it is much louder than the Volkswagen. Still, I like riding a school bus like a kid in the movies.

"Keli, the drug girl you are so chummy with, is a foster kid." Isabelle takes pride in unimpeachable gossip. "She has been into trouble since the day she moved here. Rumor has it that her next school offense will get her suspended. Principal Vanderbilt can't stand her purple hair. But since her rich foster parents have literally paid double for her to be admitted and taken off their hands, it's not like OEH can press charges. It's amazing what money can do for people," she reaches into her designer backpack and pulls out a pouch of chocolate espresso beans.

She's got *that* right. Isabelle is filthy rich. You can tell by her acrylic nails, diamond earrings, and designer backpack. She has many friends, good grades, and probably a bright Harvard future, just like generations of Isabelles before her. But she is still *average.* It is amazing what money *can't* do for people—even rich-kid Isabelle is not welcomed into the popular circle. I am realizing how little I know about wealth, money, and society. I have never paid much attention to these things in the past. I have got to catch up. Even the smallest freshman is aware of what's "in" and what's not. Everyone boasts identical brands, accessories, key chains. Perhaps there is an OEH handbook of what brands to wear and how to wear them—if only I could get my hands on it.

Still, I suppose people at OEH are free to make their own choices—Keli, at least, seems to be. But, practically, the boundaries of an American private school demark a tyranny of fashion. My wardrobe unintentionally revolves around black and navy. This is not good. I need to step up my game, or risk being marginalized. It's no small task. You have to consider not just colors, but fabrics, and cuts. Before National Popcorn Day, before the MLK break, before Groundhog Day, if possible, my style needs to evolve to something more…preppy.

"My dad's a heart surgeon," Isabelle sighs passively, twisting a monogrammed ring. "He takes me travelling across the country. I have a ring for like every European capital—Prague, Berlin, Warsaw…" she continues, but I am staring at Keli a few rows ahead. Her face is downcast, and she is wearing earbuds, clearly trying to escape the world around her.

Is "being a light to OEH" merely a metaphorical label to simply identify my personality? "Cool," I say to Isabelle with a distant glaze over my eyes. Life as a private schooler is more overwhelming than I ever imagined, and I have yet to even start homework or figure out how to open my locker. Even if I *did* make it in with a clique, if I did become a popular girl, would that mean I failed my actual mission? I really do not know if acceptance is the right thing to achieve. How is one supposed to connect with a purple-haired druggie, and a curly-headed rich awkward girl, and—most terrifyingly—a blond cheerleader?

Chapter 3

FIRST DAY

NOT TO DISAPPOINT Dad, but this totally feels like a movie. Here I am, front and center, flipping out my ID card to enter the intimidating glass doors that lead into the world of OEH. As the security scanner beeps and flashes green, my heart does a heel click. This is the day I have anticipated: my first day of actual classes. I am even greeted by Nate as I walk down the open staircase to the locker hall—the first mildly attractive person to recognize me. Unlike the past school day of community service, I am currently outnumbered in a sea of preppy upperclassmen. I feel like I am a real person now. A real, accepted high school girl.

I straighten my cream sweater and make sure my rings are on all the right fingers. Currently, the trend is to stack two rings on your left middle finger and one ring on your thumb, or so Isabelle shows me. Some girls double this, but I don't want to overdo it. I have even seen some girls reverse this order on their right hand, and others, copy it. My freshly washed hair is straightened and parted down the middle, accentuating my blond highlights. And, unlike my clothes for shadow day, I feel like this outfit resembles the look of the cheerleaders…at least, that is my hope. The best move I can make is impress the clique of all cliques. I will figure out the fine print later. My reasoning? They rule the school. If I can win them over, maybe I can work my way down…eventually. With a wave of approval from football quarterback Brett Cline, I confidently walk down the check-ered floor hallway—just like my vision. If this very moment has been ordained for my life since birth, there is no reason to be scared of it. OEH, here I come!

Oh, no. What is my locker number? Is it 114 or 117? I know it is a top locker near Mr. Groath's classroom door—convenient and scary—but I am failing to remember which one it is. I see the two juniors looking at me with patronizing frowns. I know what they are thinking: *"Poor little sophomore can't figure out her locker number."*

"Thanks for the support," I mutter.

"It's 117," Mabrey overhears me. She is opening the locker next to mine. I have never been more relieved to see her downtrodden self. How does she know my...?

"If you're ever unsure, just check all of them," pops in Keli, whose locker is below mine.

Oh, great. If there was ever a person who would smuggle drugs into my locker, it is Keli. "Happy Tuesday!" I say like we're best friends.

"Later losers." She gathers her books and slams her locker, rel-ishing a cherry sucker.

"Look at my awful tan lines! If only we could have gone to the beach for a day..." A voice sings.

"Duck and cover. They're back." Mabrey flees the scene.

I recognize that all too familiar voice giggle across the hall. And here the classes split.

Welcome back, Carissa Carlyle.

I do not know whether to turn around and pretend we're best friends, or for the sake of her popularity, act like we have never met before. I am beginning to panic. *What if I say the wrong thing? What if she humiliates me because she is with her friends?* She is coming closer down the hall. There is no time to plan an escape. I am going to have to risk it.

"Hi Carissa," I casually slam my locker.

She spins on her heel. "Oh, hey shadow. Wow...I'm liking this look you have going on," she touches my sleeve. I cannot tell if she is making fun of it or genuinely likes it. Well, this is the moment I was waiting for—her approval. I tried on at least a dozen shirts this morning trying to find something Carissa-ish, feeling like a real loser in the process. *So much for being original.*

"You remember Claire Dean, don't you girlie?" She steals a strand of my hair to twirl.

That model girl I saw last December is standing next to her, and it makes me choke on my own breath. My recovery is hardly discreet. She is even more glamorous now than when I saw her enter the math classroom with a boy at either side. Now, she has a natural, flawless tan, and her beach-blond mane of hair that falls to her waist is nearly as long as Carissa's.

"Think she's in one of your classes. Lucky her." Carissa winks. Claire throws a three-fingered wave of acknowledgment in my direction, as if she never does the talking for herself but has appointed Carissa as her entourage. Then I hear a click-click noise behind me, and in the eyes of Carissa and Claire, I become transparent.

"Let's go!" Callie Winters squeals, running to us in catwalk heels. She is petite and feisty, probably the least intimidating cheerleader of the trio. But they're all sharks.

As Callie pulls Carissa's hand, Carissa looks back at me as if she suddenly thought of something gross. "You don't need to shadow me anymore, do you?"

"Oh, don't worry about me." I beam a glamorous grin.

Carissa quickly flashes a gracious smile of relief, throwing her chin up like a girl in a lipstick commercial before running to catch up with Claire and Callie. And then, studying the empty hallway, I realize I am completely clueless about where to go for my first hour class.

I have less than a minute to figure it out.

"Sign-ups for girls track and field are in Coach Stanley's classroom tonight at 6:00 p.m. Be sure to have your sports physicals to the office by February 12th." Mrs. Gray's loud-speaker voice hums throughout Mr. Groath's somnolent classroom.

"Any fanatics who want to go kill themselves are more than welcome to," he jabs, slamming the door. It was not hard finding his class. All you had to do was look for the window covered by the giant poster of a math equation. It has the word GROATH spelled in big, black letters above the entry, like an evil doctor's office. I already feel like he is out to get me.

I look around the classroom and it is clearly obvious that I am the only sophomore in here. This is one of those moments I wish I wasn't 5'9" and didn't look like a college student. It makes teachers think I am smarter than my grade level. Does he know I once got an 'F' in math in fourth grade? 'F' as in *FAILURE?!*

"Well, well, well, class…looks like we have us a soph-a-more," he saunters to the desk I strategically chose in the back of the classroom. "Welcome to Groath's Math, which basically means, *freshmen*-level math. Tell me, Miss Gibbons, what is your current relationship status with math?" He shakes my clammy hand, emphasizing the word like I am a delinquent.

I feel like one. "I guess I am more of an English student, sir."

"That's what they all say: '*Math is too hard. I can't comprehend it,*'" he mocks in a baby voice. "For those of you who feel like Miss Gibbons, listen up." He flings a marker at an empty desk. Everyone jumps. "Math is all about the formulas," he draws a bunch of symbols unknown to me on the marker board. "But, once you master the rules, you are unstoppable." He circles his math equation. Then he drops the dreaded textbooks on our desks…the ones Carissa mentioned. Thank goodness his classroom is close to my locker so I can slip it in and out and not carry around his textbook, shouting to the world I am behind in math and belong to the freshman math class. But that is not the only unnerving factor here; the real test of fire will be the day he asks me to come up and do a problem in front of the class. The tension is building.

"The day ended with Pre-AP Bio, where I sat at one of those countertop tables that have a sink built in. Four people were grouped to a desk, and I knew literally no one because it is a freshmen class. I sat with three tiny cheerleaders who were coloring biology sketches with their little glitter pins. They kept giggling and whispering to each other. And then the teacher said, 'You're in Pre-AP Biology, so I expect each of you to perform as straight-A students.' Kelly, why in the world did you recommend that class?" I let out a long breath, recounting my day in the car.

Kelly laughs. "It was not *that* bad."

"What was wrong with it, Candice?" Mom asks, pulling into our rental house neighborhood. Driving up our steep driveway with the big bump in it makes me cringe. We have to use the emergency brake every time we park, and my water bottle has a habit of rolling down into the street when I get out. It reminds me of our lives right now—a steep, impossible hill.

"That—what I just said! That's what's wrong with it! The teacher is literally a genius." Her words fly out fast faster than I can blink. She's already planned a quiz for Friday, and I'm thinking, *a quiz over what?* There's more of a chance I'd go become a massage therapist than become an A$^+$ science student. It will take every ounce of brain power to get a passing grade."

"So dramatic." Says Kelly.

"Why don't you talk to Mrs. Gray about switching to regular biology?"

"This isn't homeschool, Mom. That would mess up my class schedule," I hastily pull out the scrap piece of paper.

"Let me see," Mom reaches.

1st Hour: World History
2nd Hour: Journalism
3rd Hour: Bible
4th Hour: Pre-AP English
5th Hour: OK History
6th Hour: Algebra
7th Hour: Pre-AP Biology

"But on second thought, it seems like my only option."

"What is?"

"Coach Stanley might let me switch my first and last class, I guess."

"I think that is up to Mrs. Gray."

"Yes, you would need to ask her first." Kelly agrees.

"Oh, great. Mrs. Gray hates me."

"You don't know that…"

"But I guess I have no choice. I've got to escape before the test."

"Mm-hm," Kelly nods. "Better do it sooner than later."

"Oh, Mom, I need to go back to the school tonight."

"Why?"

"I am signing up for track."

Sure, I am. Can I even run a lap around the track without stopping? Probably not. Then again, why shouldn't I join track? Here I am in Oklahoma with no image to obtain. Why not branch out and try something new? I guess the whole screws-in-my-feet ordeal is enough to make me reconsider, but I want to be remembered as a fighter, not an invalid. Track is both a declaration to others and a statement to myself. I took Mom's advice and asked Mrs. Gray if I could switch to regular biology, and thankfully, she let me switch my first and last hour, so now I end my school day in Mr. Stanley's hot-topic World History classroom.

Right now, he is *Coach* Stanley, and his boisterous, elderly voice draws me into his dimly lit classroom in the dark winter evening. The halls are empty and echoey, aside from a lone janitor hazily mopping the floors of the moonlit atrium. Coming to OEH outside of school hours gives me the sensation of being an 'insider,' which is nice for a change.

But as I enter the actual classroom, adorned with college track and field posters of Olympic-looking runners, I feel like anything but an insider. Catching glares from an ultra-athletic girl to my right is enough to make me sweat. Her calves are practically bulging out of her skin-tight leggings, which I can tell from the logo are ridiculously expensive. She crosses her arms and looks me up and down, probably noting my unathletic stature. Coach Stanley is passing around a clipboard with a gridded paper of rows pertaining to certain distances. Who knows what kind of a coach he is going to be, old and unfiltered?

"What do you run?" Emma, the deep-voiced junior who could easily pass for a college student, hands me the clipboard once she is finished.

What do I 'run?' What's that supposed to mean? I do not know whether to play innocent or act like I know what I am doing, but I suppose I should play it safe. "I have never done track. Would you mind explaining what these numbers mean here? What does 'm' stand for?"

"See here. If you're good at short distance, then you'll run sprints, which is either the 100-meter race, the long stretch of the track, or the 200-meter race, or '200-m,' which is half a lap. And then there's the dreaded 400m…"

"Which is a whole lap," a tall girl with brown curls tucked under her ears, pipes in, giving me a friendly smile.

Where have I seen her before?

"I'm Mika, by the way." She returns the clipboard to Coach Stanley. By her confidence and mature posture, I bet she is a senior.

Of course! She's one of the weekly news reporters in Journalism class! Short races sound good to me.

Mika is slim and pale with squared shoulders. I notice how all of the girls step back when she walks in front of them. She must be captain of the track team, or something like that. It is probably best I make friends with her if I want to survive track. She seems cool.

"Team, this season is going to be siracha good. We've got senior Mika McClain as our long-distance champion…" the room erupts in applause. "With juniors Jaden Powell, Kinsley Meyers, and Emma Baldwin as our sprinters, and, oh, I see tons of freshman names on here…Stella George and Eliza Sullivan…and, hmm…this is ooey-gooey strange. Strange like the homes the Aztecs built in the 15th century." Coach Stanley pauses and flips through the pages on the clipboard. The freshman girl, whom I am guessing is Stella, has humongous biceps and is glaring back at me. Her face matches the words on her tee shirt: "YOU'RE THE PROBLEM."

"Hmm...Candice," Coach Stanley says, and now everyone's staring at me confused. "It looks like you're our only sophomore girl runner this year."

"Oh, haha." My chuckle is met by an awkward silence, aside from the smacking of Kinsley's gum.

So much for making friends at track.

"Okay, ladies, listen up. Pre-season workouts begin tomorrow. Until March we will meet on Mondays, Tuesdays, and Thursdays in the weight room, but we'll end at the track. Park above the track on the hill by the back entrance of the school. Whoever drives the Infiniti, *please* don't park by the curb like last season or else I will personally tow it away. And everyone, please be on time changed and ready to go by 3:20." Coach Stanley stretches his arms.

Stella jumps off the top of a desk and claps, "Peace, homies."

Other athletic girls slap shoulders and say things like, "Let's go!"

The sooner I am familiar with the track lingo the better. I hold my hand up to join in the high fives, but nobody returns the gesture. Feeling awkward, I grab my backpack and start to leave the room when Coach Stanley taps my shoulder. "Hey Archie's friend, don't be discouraged. We need a sophomore representative. Man, your grade sure is weird!"

"So I am gathering,"

"We haven't had any new runners here since, well..."

"Since that new girl from California moved in and out last spring," Emma yells from the back, unpropping her feet from a desk. "She was a riot."

"Yeah, let's just say she should've joined another sport...after throwing up on her blocks right before running the 200-meter race."

"It's because she was drunk the night before," Stella blurts out.

"Let's hope Candice doesn't get drunk."

Did Coach Stanley just say that? I laugh uncomfortably, because, what else can you say?

"Candice. That name reminds me of Candace..." he snaps his fingers.

"From *Phineas and Ferb.*" I help.

"No, like Queen Candace of Ethiopia." Coach Stanley pats my back. "You're royal!"

All the same, I exit the classroom feeling more like red-haired cartoon *Candace,* the only sophomore in the entire school who was foolish enough to sign up for track. The girl who signed herself up for the 100-meter dash—the fastest track event—and the 400-meter sprint—because that is what everyone else did. Like she is fast. Like she is an athlete. Like she belongs here, on the track, here, at a private school, or here, in Oklahoma. *Sure.*

The night flies by and the day flies by, and now, it is time to actually fly. Like Allyson Felix fast. If Coach Stanley only knew how inexperienced I am, maybe he would have paired me off with one of those less athletically inclined girls who probably just joined to lose weight before prom. But, alas, he told me I would be racing alongside Kinsley Meyers—the junior with Princess Ariel hair—for the first warm-up thing. Just because we are the same height and might appear to be the same size it does not mean we are the same speed.

I approach the track in too many layers; too many cotton layers too, of no-brand clothes: my mom's red, oversized sweatshirt (hooded, of course), a black, long-sleeved UV shirt, a pair of workout leggings, and a pair of overlapping shorts for coverage. I feel like Frosty the Snowman showing up to a beach party. All I can make out are sets of tan legs stretching on the red track in Lululemon shorts. Yes, it is cold, but obviously they know something I don't. How much are we going to sweat this workout, anyway?

As I walk down the sloped parking lot from the main high school building to the track, I squint my eyes to try and make out who's legs belong to who. The world is looking more like a washy landscape, like a kindergarten watercolor painting.

"Are you here for track?" A woman's voice calls.

"Yes, I am." I smile. "Candice Gibbons. Sophomore."

"Oh, you too," she says, and I squint again, realizing she was talking to Eliza Sullivan, my sister Kelly's friend, the freshman runner, who just set down her Nike sports bag on the bottom bleacher.

"Oh, hello." That was awkward.

"Hey there, I'm Coach Lakyn. I coach long distance and hurdles." She says slowly and assuredly with a dimpled smile, a head shorter than me.

"Here she is!" Coach Stanley approaches us. "Arrive *on time*." He nudges me.

My face flushes red and I start to stammer. I am not usually a late person. Was I late?

"He's joking. Everyone else was early." Coach Lakyn reads her watch in half a second, like only a coach would do.

"Ah, here come the brides," Coach Stanley says.

There they are: a tidal wave of feminine strength, arms slicing invisible boards like karate chops. And here I stand—their finish line—stagnant, overdressed, and incapable of any level of speed. This is ridiculous. Why I am I even here?

"Take a water break," Coach Stanley yells. "Take a water break."

Mika McClain, the senior, doesn't even look like she is sweating.

"Child's play," I hear her mutter to Coach Lakyn, who laughs.

"Take it easy, Mika. This is still pre-season."

"Ready?" An out-of-breath voice says behind me. I ignore it because nobody usually talks to me.

"*Ready?*" The voice says again, this time annoyed. Kinsley is pulling her coveted long hair into a smooth ponytail in front of me. I blink twice. I can tell it is Kinsley by her hair, but is she really talking to me?

"We're running together, aren't we?" She adds in a tone that hits me as patronizing.

"Oh, yeah. I think so," I smile.

"Sweet. You look fast. I'm ready for a challenge." She compliments. The deck is stacked.

"Remember, *go slow*. You have four, easy warm-up laps to run. This is just to break the ice. You're going to be sore by the third if you push yourself too hard." Coach Stanley booms.

First of all, there is nothing easy about four laps. Secondly, we are literally standing right beside him, so there is no need for a megaphone. This makes me snicker, and then I realize everyone is staring at me and no one knows why I am laughing. As I slowly reel it in, Coach Stanley's megaphone screeches, and I try to zero in on what I am about to do. This is the moment I have waited for ever since the idea to run popped in my mind last fall. This is the time when everyone will watch me run, whether I succeed or fail. And for some reason I assumed there would be a cushion time in between me signing up and me actually running, like I would have a personal trainer and 'look the part' first, not be dumped on the track looking like a girl whose workout has been a walk around the neighborhood.

Fit or not, there is no turning back now.

"Go!"

Everyone zooms off in scattered starts. When Kinsley bursts ahead, 'go slow' immediately means nothing to me; I am giving everything I have got to catch up with her. This is a competition for my pride. My heart is pounding a thousand beats a second and my chest burns from the January wind. My feet are already pulsing with pain. We're only on our first lap. "Run faster, Candice. You don't have to go *that* slow." Coach yells from the inner field.

Run faster? I can barely step one foot in front of the other! *"Good...job,"* I say in between breaths. Kinsley passes me without giving so much as a side-glance. I would be lying if I said I did not let it get to me. What was Candice *thinking* joining this horrible sport? Why couldn't she join cheer with Carissa and dance her way to popularity? My grandmother, Gigi, had it right all along: *"Why would you kill yourself with track?"*

Track is running to your death. A *slow* death. With every step, my chest tightens, my legs twitch, and my poor, crying feet sear with pain. Maybe I should take Carissa up on that cheer offer while it stands. Cheer sounds like a breeze compared to track conditioning...

Focus, Candice. I need to focus on finishing the last lap before I become a laughingstock to the track girls and my history teacher.

"Finish strong!" Coach Lakyn calls out to me, and I realize I am the only one still on the track. I see some girls crossing their arms and whispering about me at the finish line.

I collapse mid-stride when I reach the end, bracing my tall self with my hands before hitting the ground.

Clap. Clap. Clap. A few girls offer halfhearted sympathy applause before turning to grab their bags. Well, there we have it. There is no sense in hiding how unpolished of a runner I am. I throw my bag over my shoulder and walk over to Coach, shoulders trembling.

"I've…been…meaning to tell you, I have pins in both of my feet…this is my first time to run. I, ugh…used to be a dancer, but I had to quit after surgery…"

Stella and some other freshman girls are listening. I can't tell if they're inspired or disgusted. Even juniors Emma and Kinsley stopped on their way off the track to hear the end. But at this point, I don't really care about what other girls think about how I am joining to overcome a lifelong battle with my feet. I want to be able to conquer something. And, well, if I die in the process, at least I put up a fight. Track is the perfect distraction from the pain of leaving Missouri and the rejection of lonely walks down checkered-floor halls.

I really should journal about the past three days, but my brain feels like an overheated hard drive. I considered an audio entry, but then again, I don't know if I want to verbally recount how I totally mishandled cues and codes. Hopefully, the embarrassing things are behind me now.

Aside from OEH, I feel confused, lonely, and sad. I miss sitting in Mom and Dad's old bedroom where we used to have deep chats. I long to see the Bricks, my old friend group, at school. Like, what if they walked with me to my locker every day? Surely, I would be popular—accepted. I try to imagine what Diana would say if she was with me throughout my day. She would probably support me if I said I wanted to drop out.

But I can't drop out! Where would I go? OEH is at least like a safety net where I don't have to face upside-down, everyday home life in the rental house. It is not as if I can crash at my grandparents' houses anymore. I can't spend the night at the farm and run away from the big and scary world. Thankfully, I did not come here out of my own will, but God's. I can't quit because I have had a hard first week. God is going to bless me for being obedient and moving to Oklahoma. The question is, can I survive the next two and a half years of high school at OEH?

"Don't forget what your name means," Dad tells me when I hug him goodnight. "You are 'Full of Light.' You are a light to your school! There are always opportunities to make a difference in the world. It starts with one-on-one interactions with people. Surely there's someone God wants you to reach at OEH."

But who?

Chapter 4

HOMECOMING

DRESSED AS AN alien wearing a foil headband, a blue tie dye sweatshirt, and neon pink rainboots, I approach the door to what I think is my Bible class. My first clue something isn't right is when I open it to students who are definitely not my classmates.

"Can we help you?" The teacher suppresses a smile.

The word 'we' makes the whole class turn to see the intruder. The girls look me up and down. Some boys start to snicker. My face burns red.

This is definitely not my class.

The school bulletin board says it is spirit week, and Monday's theme read 'Dress Like an Alien.' It feels like I am the only sophomore who took the bait. And I thought I was over embarrassing situations. "I'm sorry...I'm in the wrong place." I quickly shut the door, squeaking down the halls to my second option: Journalism class. The bell has already rung, but part of me doesn't even care. I accidentally deleted the picture I snapped of my class schedule, and I would rather stall classroom time and figure out the route out on my own rather than walk to the office and get a lecture from Mrs. Gray on time management and ownership.

Hysterically, there is a horizontal banner lining the balcony railing of the atrium painted for spirit week reading *"OEH: Happiest*

Place on Earth. "I laugh and run my fingers along the paper. The halls are dark and eerily lit with florescent hues from overhead lights filtered with pink, green, and blue tissue paper. The checkered ground now reflects shiny shades that remind me of the cover of a VHS aerobics tape from the '80s. Alien cut-outs adorn the walls, watching me and my munchy boots on the waxed floor. *Squeak. Squeak. Squeak.* The seniors are probably laughing at me. No; the whole school—right down to the Pre-AP Bio freshmen girls with their glittery pens and Lululemon lunch sacks. I open the door to Journalism class, and partly to my relief, partly to my grief, it is empty.

"Nice costume!" Mrs. Lajuana glances up from her computer. "But you're here during my off hour?"

"So sorry to bother, but I'm completely lost." I refer to my literal state of being directionally lost, and subconsciously to my emotional state of feeling out of place.

"Class schedule?" Mrs. Lajuana rises from her desk and stretches. Today she displays wooden beads in her hair and a thick ginger turtleneck. She smells like burnt orange peels and Thieves. I see oil marks on her neck and wrists.

"Mine? Oh, ugh, I accidentally lost the paper version. I also deleted the screenshot off my phone. I'm really sorry to bother. I know it must be weird that I'm lost even though I've been here for a while now. That goes to show how new I am at this."

"At what, spirit week?" She laughs again, eying my rubber boots.

"Well, yeah. Honestly, everything. I've never had to navigate a big school like this before. I was homeschooled." The foil I wove around my headband is starting to unravel and it is making my ear itch. I try to fix it, but I end up tearing off a triangle. It falls to the floor, a silver slate of pixie dust.

"Bahhh," She excuses my fears with the wave of her hand. "You'll get used to OEH. And I suggest not deleting that picture off your phone, young journalist. You never know what you may need in the future. Your brain," she taps her head, "is a hard drive. Your devices," she points to her computer, "are your stocks. Your bonds. Your..." she searches for the right word. "Eh, come with me, I will walk you to the office."

I am content with that. From now on, I will remember to carefully sort and retain information like I am a file cabinet. I may not be administratively inclined, but I am a journalist—a storyteller—and I must guard my memories like food, like sleep, like time. With resolve to do just that, I straighten my sweatshirt, square my shoulders, and walk on my tiptoes to avoid too harsh of a squeaking sound.

We learn from a very annoyed and ever-so-graying Mrs. Gray I am supposed to be in my new biology class. Mrs. Lajuana's bronze hand volunteers to walk me there.

"Do you have an explanation for being late?" My new science teacher asks, pausing at the board. All young sets of curious eyes turn around to stare at the sophomore dressed as an alien in the doorway.

"I needed to speak with her before class," Mrs. Lajuana vouches.

I could cry with thankfulness.

February has begun, and we are counting down two weeks to Valentine's Day: the most dreaded day of the year. I am sitting in Oklahoma History class pre-living how lonely today's lunch is going to be when I walk to the cafeteria in the drizzling sleet to gnaw on a soggy cream cheese and strawberry jelly sandwich all by myself. I am also already anticipating the roses and chocolates and cards that will be passed around by secret admirers to clusters of blushing cheerleaders from the sports jocks on that dreaded day while I sit forlorn in the corner of the classroom with crossed fingers and unmet relational expectations. That is literally what it is going to be like. Maybe I will get sick on Valentine's Day. Then I won't have to smile and act happy when the freshmen girls in math class come up to me and ask how many love notes I've received...which will be none.

"Candice, right?"

"Yeah."

"Want to come to lunch with Carey, Morgan, and I?" Afton, the tall basketball player, says after I emerge from Oklahoma History. I blink twice. We just watched a traumatizing video of wartime surgeries pre-anesthesia, and I can't get the last graphic scene out of my head. She is asking me while we walk down the concrete set of stairs in a sea of noisy, hungry teenagers, and I barely hear her. But when you're starving for affection, you're not deaf enough to miss an invitation—especially with someone above average. Afton is in the popular group but not a popular girl, if that makes sense. Regardless, she is higher ranked than Isabelle or Keli.

Today's theme is Dress Like a Superhero, and I am dressed as Violet Parr from *The Incredibles*. I do resemble her closely: my dark hair is mid-length and straight, partly shielding my eyes, and let's face it, I might as well be invisible at OEH. I bend a stray piece of hair behind my ear.

"Sure," I say nonchalantly, like I might have better options, but sure, I will go with her. Afton is actually a lifesaver. Emerging from the staircase, we enter the famous hallway of red lockers. Mine is down about sixteen on the left. I walk slowly because I am not sure where Afton's locker is and where she is about to stop, and I do not want to appear to be rushing off like I have somewhere to go, because I don't. I casually grab my wallet and slam my locker door, feeling like a really cool high schooler walking through the crowded school hallways beside Afton. All of the students are escaping in BMW's extra happily today since it is Thursday, and sophomores are—legally— allowed to ride to lunch with upperclassmen.

Sweat-suited Morgan is outside standing next to Carey's Tesla. Carey is a junior and a cheerleader, and by those titles, she sounds cool. But she is really just slightly above-average in a no-nonsense, patronizing adult sense, and I think she would find my hyper-active imagination overstimulating. I do not see this blossoming into a future friendship. Still, I thank her for the invitation and compliment her hair and nails and everything we OEH girls are supposed to do as we get in her tinted-window car, and she cranks up loud pop music and we swerve out of the parking lot. I text Mom to tell her we are going to Parsley Bowl for lunch and that a responsible (or at least, I think she is?) upperclassman is driving the car.

"Oops," Carey bumps the curb right before we merge onto the highway.

I clutch a nearby handle lit with a pink LED spotlight shining the BMW logo on her custom-fitted floormats. My heart is pounding so fast. I could not be more excited and alarmed. The lyrics to her playlist are embarrassingly vulgar, and I feel a bit incriminated. Like, what would my friends in Missouri say about me, Violet Parr, bumping along an Oklahoma City service road to the soundtrack of a breakup song? This whole situation is uncomfortable, but not in the unfamiliar sense where you just have to get used to it to become comfortable, rather, the kind that makes you glad you aren't in these situations very often. And let's face it; I have never really driven before, but right now, I am quickly planning on what I would do if something happened, because Morgan is totally unaware and focused on her phone, and Afton is jamming out. I fiddle with my bracelet.

"D'you know this song?" She bobs her head car dancing.

"No," I yell confidently. Get a clue—I wouldn't be caught *dead* singing these lyrics!

We pull into Parsley Bowl's parking lot just as Morgan mutters aspirations about her ideal boyfriend. When we get out, it is all too fun to feel normal. I can only help but sense...

Of course.

Carissa is walking in with Callie and Claire. Callie whispers to Carissa when they see me. *What are they saying? What do they think of me? Ugh. Why did I dress up? Why didn't I just dress normal?* Of course, they are not dressed as superheroes. They probably think they *are* superheroes—like everyone should dress like them.

"You're up," Carey says, pushing me forward.

Now I realize I have been holding up the line while studying Carissa's designer sneakers. As I order some Greek rice, the only recognizable thing I can spot on the menu, I fumble for my wallet and melt. I can't feel a single dollar bill. *Didn't I put the $20 Dad gave me in the zipper pocket?* It's not there. I can't feel any money. *What am I going to do?*

"Here," Carey shoves a twenty to the cashier with a side glance at me.

"Oh no, Carey, I can find it..."

"Don't worry about it," she says with a peeved lip smile.

"I'll pay you back."

"Seriously, it's nothing." She rolls her eyes and returns her Louis Vuitton wallet to her oversized jacket pocket. She's right; a twenty is probably nothing to her.

Swallowing feelings of inferiority, I walk my steamy bowl of rice to the modern white table that everyone's gathered around trying to appear cool. But on the inside, I am a nervous wreck. Everything is blurry and wishy-washy like a bad dream, and I can just feel the tension that everyone is probably looking at me like I am poverty level.

The basketball girls, Morgan and Afton, have been waved over to join the cheer booth, which means Carey the junior and Candice the sophomore are—by association—invited there, too. It is like our BMW caravan is a little clique in of itself. It matters what car you are in. Like, Isabelle may drive a Range Rover, but she's no good here. We'd be in a corner booth next to some average boys if I stepped foot in here with her. You really must watch yourself.

The good news? Carey is wearing a Captain America windbreaker in half-participation of spirit week, like most upperclassmen who participate in an *I'm-too-old-for-this-yet-will-do-it-as-favor-to-the-world* attitude. But whether her heart is in it or not, it helps me look less awkward. I'll take it.

"Are you excited for homecoming?" Claire, the classiest of all the cheerleaders, asks the group. When she speaks, all forks freeze midair, and all heads lift like eager deer. She has that kind of presence. Astonishingly, Claire herself is actually wearing a Wonder Woman bracelet in subtle participation. I know it seems small, but it is the small things that matter at OEH—right down to the length of your nails. Some girls wear nail tips, which is like a layer of plastic added to the end of your nail to make them look longer. But Claire is not wearing tips, and ironically, she seems to be the only one who doesn't have a problem with me. Not yet.

I smile and nod at her question, playing with my rice. I *am* really excited about homecoming this weekend. I love breaking up the normalcy of school. I am hoping this week it will break the ice in one way or another. And seeing Claire's bracelet gives me hope like she might be a kindred spirit, like she might like *me*.

"You know, Candice," Callie leans over and whispers in her high-pitched valley girl voice. "If you join cheer, you get invited to all of these exclusive activities—like parties with the popular kids." She winks at me. "Even some seniors come!"

"Oh," I smile before taking a long sip of icy cold water. I try not to gag. I wish I could see all of this clearly. Do I *want* to be a popular kid? Who wouldn't?! But our whole grade—the whole school for that matter—associates cheerleaders with mean human beings because that is what they are. I am trying to be a light to the school, not just fit in with a little clique. *But is this really a clique?* I mean, Carey and Afton and Morgan are decently normal. It's not like they wear tips on their nails. And look at my other options: Keli is more likely to get me kicked off the track team by drug-dealer association and Isabelle has her own group of average kids like Mabrey—who clearly don't want anything to do with me. *What's a girl to do?*

I finally found my vision.

"The leaves! Each in their own crystal green shape, so majestic, so…so…"

"You act like you have never seen a tree before," Mom laughs.

"Because I haven't! Not like this, anyway."

Look out, everyone. Candice just got contact lenses—an extreme deficiency has been met—and now the world is a bustling parade. This has got to help me in more ways than one. Maybe I will no longer be invisible to OEH. Maybe I will be able to actually see the world at a new level. I am alive. I am real. *I can see!*

"Candice and Allister, you two will cover the basketball homecoming game footage. Your video needs to be submitted on Friday by the end of the day. *Capisce?*" Mrs. Lajuana writes our names in red on the marker board with the words "HOCO Game" beside them. It literally takes me a minute to figure out what HOCO means. Still, at least I can read the words from the back of the classroom. I feel so alert and clear-minded. Who knew I was blind?

"Teach, I ain't goin'." Allister says. It doesn't surprise me. He is wearing a green "Gamer" shirt, he has curled his legs up around his arms like a contortionist, and his droopy bangs are flopped over his eyes. He really loves life.

"Fine. But no extra credit for the upcoming newscast." Mrs. Lajuana erases his name from the list of journalism reporters. "Candice," she points to an unimpressed junior slurping a Starbucks in the back of the classroom. "You'll go with Harper."

"Wha?" Her hair is greasily falling in her face, and she is wearing a wrinkly oversized *Buc-ee's* shirt.

Oh, please no. I swivel my gaze to Mrs. Lajuana with a silent, desperate cry for someone else, but Mrs. Lajuana merely grins at me with a sparkle in her eye. Something tells me she has given me a challenge, like she knows I will be doing 99% of this video. Maybe this is my chance to show Mrs. Lajuana what I can do with a camera. I can already picture the whole school enamored by my video, carefully watching the screens. *"Wow! Who took these incredible shots?"* Principal Vanderbilt will say, and then someone will shout, "CANDICE!" and I will be picked up in the air and carried around OEH. And then everyone will want to be my friend and I will make a difference at school. *Yeah, right.*

The basketball arena is roaring with Redbull-infused, crimson-faced teens. The bleachers are patterned with red and white school spirit shirts. All of these colors flash in my eyes like piercing laser lights, finally not in the least bit blurry. I am wearing a Journalism sticker as a press badge so I can have access to the court. I feel rather special walking in with my new school hoodie and press badge. Kelly has already found a seat next to Eliza and other safe, well-mannered, freshmen-aged girls. I, on the other hand, cannot spot an empty seat anywhere. And I can't even blame it on poor vision. Oh...Harper is texting...

She can't make it.

Are you serious? This means I am responsible for all of tonight's footage! Not only does this mean I will look like the lone reporter on the court, like, did I make up this sticker badge and have my mom print it at home? Plus, there goes my automatic seat partner. I lean on the doors that lead into the basketball court and scan my options. *Who am I going to sit with?*

After a lengthy thirty seconds I spot Afton and Carey walking up the bleachers in the student section, so I run over to them and follow them up one of the benches with expectancy.

"Oh, Candice, I don't think there's room here for one more," Afton says slowly, looking around. Well, this is awkward. If these were my friends in Missouri, we would *make* room for each other. It's just what friends do. Obviously, no one considers me a friend like that yet.

Keli is waving at me from the bleachers. "Hey! Over here!" She looks a lot older without pigtails, but she still has her purple hair. "Come sit with us!" She runs over and pulls me by the hand before I have a chance to answer or see Morgan and Afton's expressions. Keli stops at a top bleacher where a few of the druggie boys are sprawled out. "You remember these guys from Pre-AP English, Isaac and Kenny?" Oh, sure I remember them. Isaac and Kenny smell like smoke. They write stories on Godzilla and holographic plants with monster capabilities. They are probably all destined to accompany Keli and her boyfriend tonight to smoke weed or do something else back-alleyish. Everything in me tells me to get off the bleacher and run to the other side but wait—that is all of the cheerleaders right across from us! Which is worse?!

"Oh, you don't have to sit with us..." Keli says in a disappointed voice, eying me as I look longingly to the other side.

Cheerleaders never looked so safe. But here I go again assuming things. I need to give Keli the benefit of the doubt. I am supposed to be a light to OEH. "It's cool. But I do need to get some shots in a minute," I say. The basketball players are huddling up. I have never covered basketball game clips before, but my instinct tells me I should gather pre-game footage. I slip away from the drug crowd and walk around the court exposing myself to the masses so I can get to the players. But before I do, I have to pass the girls who are cheering for this game.

"Hey, Candice."

Did someone just say my name? I turn around and see none other than Carissa standing in her glittery red and white, skin-tight cheer uniform. I can't believe she said my name out loud. I would have expected her to ignore me, like she has pretty much ever since I started walking with Keli from class to class. What is she up to?

"Hi Carissa!" I wave back. And then she giggles something to Callie. Of course. I start to walk away from them when a cheerleader's white-sleeved arm touches my shoulder.

"Getting shots for Journalism?" says a smooth voice.

"Um, yeah!" I blush.

"Good luck," Claire smiles. Having her attention, I nearly miss getting the shots I need. The five-minute warning buzzer goes off and alerts me.

"Um, I gotta go get shots…good luck to you too!" If I can become friends with Claire, maybe I could secure a spot on the cheer team, and then the rest of high school would be a breeze. I would automatically have friends, activities—everything! Thinking of this puts a skip in my step, and I decide to break out of my shell and ask the basketball team if I can film a specific shot before the game starts.

"Hey guys," I say. "Um, excuse me…" Nobody hears me.

"Excuse me," I yell, and now they look at me like I am their mom trying to get a picture. "I am going to take the camera down the row, so everyone act 'hyped up' for the game. Three…two… one…" No one even looks at the camera.

"One more time. More hype, please," I say, this time in a loud and commanding tone. This is the first time I have heard my inner leader voice post leaving Missouri.

To my amazement, this shot of the players actually turns out really well. I thank the team and get some close court shots the rest of the night, eventually sitting beside Keli until the end of the game.

Once the stadium begins to clear, I say goodbye to Keli casually yet purposefully, walking slowly down the court while I contemplate my next move. I overhear students talking about a party that is happening in an old barn close to the school.

"Are you going?" Claire says behind me. Here is my opportunity to step in and experience what OEH is truly like—my long-awaited chance to get in with the cool kids! "You can ride with me, if that's what you're worried about," she adds, walking beside me.

I am going to my first party!

I don't know what I was expecting. It's like…a party. The base is loud and deafening. Strobe lights spin around the room. I barely see anything but the silhouettes of teenagers dancing by the DJ's table. Claire did not mention Stevie Bowers, the boy who strikes me as a rhino and calls me Cassidy, would drive us to the party, but thankfully it was not very far from the school, and I survived. Of course, they both left me to dance as soon as we arrived. It figures.

"Yo!" Yells a familiar voice behind me. I make out Stella's figure, the freshman star on the track team. "I just got here." She unzips her sports jacket and throws it in a corner.

"I think everyone's just kind of dancing," I say neutrally. "I'm not really…"

"Then let's join them!" She yells, pulling me into the crowd of dancers.

I laugh and try to look disinterested. She twirls my arm and then does her own little shake, and I start to jump awkwardly, unable to match the beat.

"This isn't OEH anymore, you know. Rules don't apply off school campus." Stella grins mischievously.

I have gathered that much. Claire is dancing bad with the basketball players. All the cheerleaders are doing it. But, like Stella said, this party is unaffiliated with OEH. I can't believe I was gullible enough to come to this in the first place. Well, here I am, compromising my values by walking in with Claire and endorsing this party like it's all fine and good.

But what if I'm wrong? What if I've lived life too sheltered until now? How am I supposed to make a difference in my school if I can't get down on everyone's level? Maybe I am being too innocent. After all, I have to show I am relatable. I slow down my jumping pace and Stella leaves me to go dance with some other freshmen. Now Claire is looking at me with an *are you okay?* expression. I smile and grab a red plastic cup of punch from the table next to me, raising it in the air to show I am having a good time. Because I am. I think I am.

Chapter 5

THE INVITATION

"WOW, A WHOLE bouquet of roses! They're so... pretty!" I try to flash a genuine smile at Carissa in the hall. Everything is just like I assumed: I am spending the holiday without a single rose of admiration, and this year, I don't even have the Bricks with whom to share singleness sympathy.

Happy Valentine's Day, Candice. Happy Valentine's Day.

"If only I could figure out who they came from..." Carissa surveys several onlookers.

"They're from me," Brett Cline taps her on the shoulder. He swishes his curly hair to the side, revealing a striking set of green eyes, flashing like twinkling lights against his olive skin. This is no surprise. Of course, it was Brett Cline. And, of course, Brett Cline and Carissa Carlyle would be together. It is the perfect quarterback-cheerleader combination. I would be a little disappointed if he fell for anyone else. This is perfect, and this is also my perfect chance to slip away before I am caught in a circle of cheerleaders. I don't want to look completely helpless when I open up my locker to nothing but Mr. Groath's purple and orange textbook dutifully waiting on me. On the front of his textbook is a cartoon character of a black mouse with pointy ears, slits for eyes and two sharp teeth. I imagine the mouse laughing at me every time I pick it up. I am surprised it hasn't appeared in one of my dreams yet.

"Why did you come?" Says an eerie voice behind me.

Speaking of creepy, it is a boy named Dillon, a very, very strange character. He warned me last year when I shadowed Carissa not to come to OEH. "I'm sorry?" I hold my breath to keep cool.

"I told you this is a bad school. You shouldn't have…"

"Yo, that's my locker," Keli pushes past me.

And once again, Dillon vanishes down a hall.

This isn't the first time I have opened Keli's locker. Come to think about it, something smells strange under the wadded up black jacket on top of her books. They should really consider putting combination locks on our lockers for the sake of kids like me who have to share spaces next to drug dealers and possible thieves. I quickly shut the door and pretend not to notice. Keli has been avoiding me ever since the homecoming party when Claire posted a picture of the event and I happened to be in the background dancing with Stella. At first, I was horrified, but I soon realized Keli was probably the only one who would have been bothered I was there, and only because she had not been formally invited. Regardless, she probably would have turned down the invitation. The whole situation confuses me.

As I open locker 117—my locker—I see a crumpled heart-shaped cookie with frosty pink icing sitting atop my books with a friendly, cliché poem attached. I didn't even notice Keli stopped to watch me. "It's from me," she says.

"Wow, really? Oh, thank you!" I smile, and then hesitate when I realize she wants me to eat it, because I don't eat sugar on track days. Discipline makes me feel like a real athlete. Besides, what if she put something in it? You can never be too careful… "I will eat this as a reward for myself after track practice!"

Her smile vanishes. "I know it's nothing much. I only gave one to you and Allister."

All of a sudden, I see this innocent, childlike innocence hidden behind purple bangs. "You are so sweet to think of me." I hastily add. "Did you know you're the only person who gave me a Valentine today?" I try ignoring the fact that Carissa and Callie are watching us.

"No," she says with a hint of surprise in her voice, shuffling her black boots and sticking her hands in the pockets of her charcoal leather jacket. "I assumed…"

"And this is extra special because I'm a new kid and all. This means a lot," I clutch my books and lean my head against the locker, feeling mature and secure and even a bit older, like a seventeen-year-old. Keli nods reflectively and walks off with a softer face than when she first approached me. I hope my words were even a little bit encouraging.

My confidence sways as I walk to Mr. Groath's classroom. The gossip train has begun, tooting and chugging with all the cheerleaders' opinions.

"Did you see that? Candice and Keli are friends!"

"Keli the foster kid?"

"Maybe it was a drug handoff."

"Candice can't make up her mind on her popularity stance…"

"I know, right?"

But I just smile and continue walking. It is not my problem—not *our* problem as new kids—to sort out the truth with everyone in the school. It's impossible. Still, a tiny dark cloud settles on me. Mika passes me on the left, but I don't even bother to look up. She is already surrounded by an adoring fan club of admirers. To her, I am just another face in the crowd. And honestly, deep down, I am starting to feel like I know less and less about who I am. Dillon may have a point.

"You joined at the perfect time." Mrs. Abernathy lays a book on my desk in Pre-AP English. "We are starting a new book called *Things Fall Apart* by Chinua Achebe."

"Cool." I suppress a laugh. Is this some kind of joke?

"Everyone turn to chapter one. Let's get some things straight. Iguedo is the village. Okonkwo is the main character. Say it with me—'Ok*ooo*nkwoah'."

"Ok*ooo*nkwoah."

I am in a daze sucking on tiny chocolate pretzel balls thinking about the letter O and this African novel from the 1950s. *Things Fall Apart.* If this title does not fit my life right now, I don't know what does. You really can't make this stuff up.

Mrs. Abernathy props her plentiful self to a metal stool in the right-hand corner of the classroom. "Achem. Read with me." She throws her dangling tie-dye shawl over her shoulder.

Okonkwo. Okonkwo. Okonkwo. I munch the chocolate balls, drifting into an imaginary jungle with a man running from a tribal leader who happens to have long blond hair. *Okonkwo…klahoma… oeh…* That creepy mouse on my math notebook—I see him, too. And Dillion is hiding in the bushes. Is this still Valentine's Day? Oh, my word. It is taking forever to end. *Run, Okonkwo. Run far, far away.* I slide lower in my seat, losing myself to an amazon of thoughts about this truly collapsing life of mine.

"Hey Cassidy, I like your shirt." Stevie says. I know he is talking to me. He renamed me after he was over the whole "you look like Emma Watson" repetitive comment. I kept clarifying I really don't look like her. Now, we're back to Cassidy. It fits. 'Candice' is becoming such a vague, past-tense figure of Missouri's aging history. I kind of feel like I am a 'Cassidy' now; Cassidy, the soon-to-be cheerleader at one of the richest schools in the state.

Stevie—however awkward—is acting awfully uncharacteristic dealing out compliments, especially to me. *No one* acknowledges me in third hour Bible class—not by Emma or Cassidy or even my real name. I can't tell if he is making fun of my shirt or flirting with me. Callie Winters, who is sitting next to him, makes a quick side glance to see what I am wearing, searching for any remote sign of competition. I guess I am 'dressed up;' I borrowed my mom's scarlet flower blouse with a high neck in honor of Valentine's Day. I like it a lot, but it might come across dressy or too mature. Still, it is comfortable and flattering.

"I like it too," says Nate, Claire's boyfriend, one of those *I'm-cute-and-I-know-it* jocks.

"Thanks," I say nonchalantly, though I feel anything but casual. All of this attention from boys is making Callie and a few other girls scowl, like all of a sudden, I am the girl every guy likes—which is absolutely absurd and the *last* thing I need right now. In moments like this I wish I had worn all black to become a complete shadow to the guys.

Throughout the rest of the hour, I have a crawling worm in my stomach. I wish I could just run out of this classroom so the boys would stop analyzing me, which, by the way, they are still doing as I doodle in my notebook. *Am I overly dressed?* I think to myself, not paying attention to the Bible verse quiz paper lying on my desk. Obviously, I missed some kind of social cue that is making boys notice me and girls hate me.

The bell rings and I march out of World History class like a robot, walking up the stairs with every other OEH student right now. My brain is fried with textbook information and today's holiday social stress. I can't wait to get out of this flirty costume and change into my track clothes. I stop on the platform of the staircase to search for Mika, who is usually coming out of Physics class. I spot her standing at the edge of the staircase in a woven cherry sweater that perfectly complements her brown curls tucked around her ears. She has bright red lipstick and is laughing while her boyfriend massages her back. She is bursting with senior popularity. *Oh, if only I could be like her.* I sigh and continue up the stairs.

Thus ends my sad, sixteen-year-old Valentine's Day spent alone. At least it is over.

Valentine's Day is definitely not over.

"Mom, you will NOT believe this..." I run out of my room straight into the kitchen. She is cooking spaghetti.

"You got asked out on date?" Kelly skips into the kitchen, holding pink roses.

"Kelly? Did *you* have an admirer today?" I stare in shock at my sister's sparkly bouquet.

"In fact, I did. I turned him down, of course. But he still gave me the flowers." She smiles nervously.

Mom laughs. "What, Candice?"

I re-read the group chat message:

>*You're invited to a Galantine's dinner downtown tonight at 7p.m. Meet at the 405 Diner on Broadway. Please bring a small gift for our gift exchange. See you there!!!—Callie Winters*<

This is absolutely amazing! No way in a million years would I have thought little ol' me would be invited to an exclusive Valentine's dinner with the cheerleaders! *"I can't believe I've been invited to a Galantine's dinner!"* I say in a screech. I check the list of people invited and see it's everyone in the popular group: Carissa Carlyle, Callie Winters, Claire Dean…This is *huge!*

"Sounds like the popular girls' convention," Kelly warns with wide eyes. Even she steers away from the *Carissa Carlyle's* of her grade because of their stereotype.

"Well, what are you waiting for? Get dressed!" Mom says, which reminds me I am completely clueless what to wear. I scram to Mom's closet and search for the perfect dress—something stylish but not too formal—wishing I had saved the red blouse for tonight. Will guys be there? Should I text someone else to see what they are wearing? No, too shallow. I have to hurry! I am starting to sweat. *Not good, Candice. Chill out.* But seriously, why would I be invited after spending the whole day anonymously, being gossiped about for chatting with Keli? Is this because of the guys complimenting my outfit? Are they planning some kind of prank?!

I consider this while trying on a dozen options (and hurriedly throwing them on the ground), finally landing on a short, fuchsia-striped dress with black leggings and velvet wedges. I have exactly five minutes before we need to leave, but my makeup is only half done, and my hair is not curling—no matter how long I hold it under the curling iron. It's no use. It already smells like I burnt it. I better just drench it with hairspray and walk out the door. This is as good as it's gonna get. I still can't believe I have been invited.

Oklahoma City is bustling with Thursday night excitement. The streets are electric with music, clusters of couples, and flashing lights. On one side, you have parades of Lamborghini's and Lexus's chauffeuring bronzed businessmen in loosened collars to evening cocktails. On less highlighted sidewalks and alleys, you have the limping homeless population, dragging trash bags and grocery carts to designated benches and alley corners. I feel sick and disheartened at the needs of both populations, as both are in desperate need of satisfaction in life, and yet I do not know what to do about it. I am in need of a little help myself.

I lean my head on the frosty window and frown at my reflection. I feel more and more like this might be a set up. I mean, wasn't it just this morning I saw these girls gossiping about me when I was talking to Keli? Why would they plan this so last minute? What if nobody comes? I envision them videoing my ignorance as I walk in and out of the restaurant with my giftbag all while they are dying with laughter from their BMW's. I would not put it past them.

"Have fun!" Mom drops me off at the front entrance of the street-side restaurant.

'Have fun!'—that's a good one. This is about as fun as being set up for public humiliation. This compares to the torture of running laps at track practice. Before I grab the doorhandle, just as I learned to do when I face my fears, I pray a quick and desperate prayer for God to go with me and perhaps give me a supernatural filter of beauty.

"I'm glad someone else is here." Someone says to my right. That prayer worked fast. I spin around at the sound of a familiar voice. Morgan is sitting in a waiting chair wearing school clothes, clutching a wrinkled party bag. This is good; she looks like me and makes me feel less tall and brown, though I do feel extra dressed-up when I take a seat next to her. Still, I am thankful I have someone to sit with who isn't intimidating. She does not seem near as stuck-up as the cascade of blond cheerleaders, even if she does wear fake eyelashes.

And here they come now.

The flood of tipped-nail cheerleaders rushing through the doors makes the restaurant hush and stare. Carissa is wearing a luxury fur coat and a Gucci belt, carrying two professionally wrapped presents. Carissa and Callie have the same sort of miniskirt preppy look that reminds me of the '90s. I bet it is coming back 'in.' Claire is still wearing her school clothes, but she always dresses like she is right off an Instagram ad, so she does not look out of place. "Morgan, honey, have you ensured our reservation?" Carissa steps to the front of the group, glaring at me like I am not supposed to be here. It is funny how quickly friends can change to enemies. Carissa is *not* the same friendly tour guide I met on my first day at OEH. Come to think of it, I wonder who let Callie invite me in the first place...

"Um, it's gonna be a while," Morgan checks the wait time on her phone.

Carissa rolls her eyes at me like my presence—my extra chair— is causing the wait.

"Let's go outside and take pictures," suggests Callie, so our little party shuffles out of the restaurant and to the side of the brick building adorned with string lights and picnic tables. A jazz band is jiving on the patio of a nearby restaurant, adding background music to our fancy and stiff affair. I am shivering with nervous chills and February frost, and I immediately regret not bringing a coat, but I didn't like pairing my one and only snow coat with a stain on the back with my dress, so I left it in the car.

I am standing in the back of the group while everyone rotates with pictures, because of course no one has asked me to join them. I wonder when the tables turned, and someone lobbed up that Candice should be invited. Was it Callie in Bible class? Or perhaps Carissa herself when she got wind that Stevie liked my shirt? Maybe they thought I was some kind of threat and decided it would be safest to control me under the watchful eyes of their clique. Maybe they pictured me rounding up and stealing all their boyfriends while they went to dinner. Who knew you could be intimated by cheerleaders a head smaller than you?

"What about a group picture?" I suggest cheerily. But everyone only gives me a displeased smile and continues to take pictures with two or three girls at a time. What is wrong with them?

Oh, I get it. They don't want people to find out who they invited, so they don't want to take a group picture. Popular Girls Rule #1. I should have known. I am lost in thought, thinking back to the times I took pictures with the Bricks when *I* was the one coordinating photo shoots. Now, I am just the new girl lost in the crowd. These girls already have their own agenda; they know what they want and who they need to accomplish it. They don't need my help, and they certainly don't see how their actions are affecting me.

Yet, the night is not evil. No one does any pranks or says any particularly rude comments. In fact, I really enjoyed being included in the popular girls' group.

The entire restaurant seemed to freeze when we were escorted to our long table in the center of the restaurant, and all of a sudden, I was a rich girl—a popular girl—who lived in Oklahoma City and attended a private school. I feel under-accepted yet not completely isolated, like half of the group (the basketball girls, mainly) actually don't mind my company, and Carissa has enough friends to keep from being stuck with me. And maybe this is what it is all about, becoming popular so I can be an influence at OEH. Maybe I will start getting invited to parties more often, and soon Isabelle and Keli will see me as an asset, so I will win the approval of both the average kids and the druggies, and then, maybe I can be the light God wants me to be.

If there is one atmosphere I expect to fit in right away, it is church. I am a PK, for goodness' sake. Tonight is my first time attending our new youth group at New Life Church—the real reason our family moved here—and I am pretty certain things will feel somewhat normal again. Besides, after witnessing the homecoming party and a dinner with the cheerleaders, I feel almost guilty—like I need to clean up and spend time with other Christians before I start becoming a snob and dressing scandalously and singing explicit songs.

"Welcome to New Life Youth! You're new here, aren't you?" A leader with waist length braids high-fives me at the door to the church.

"Hi, yeah!" I step into the foyer of the church and survey the crowd of teenagers. I am the only white, brown-haired girl in sight. I introduce myself and make small talk while scanning the room for Tia Samone, the girl who helped us move into our rental house. I have never been around so much diversity in my entire life, and it is making me feel out of place, like I am the one who doesn't belong. I would give anything to have my friend, Jaclyn, here right now. *Why can't New Life Church be like my old church?* No, this is Oklahoma, not Missouri. I must accept this new culture gracefully.

"You can sit with me." The leader says to me like I am a friendless, unchurched newcomer. I almost laugh when I think about how I kind of am one. Actually, unless I find Tia soon, I will need someone to sit with, so this is good. Still, I would rather not jump in right away—making friends and commitments. I have too much on my plate with track season starting—not to mention cheer tryouts (if I decide to join). And while I hate to admit it, ever since the Valentine's Dinner, I feel somewhat superior to the world. Like I don't need any sympathy votes. Like I am a, popular girl. I don't like this side of me.

"Thanks," I smile, and as I feel it is my duty to inform her, I blurt out, "my dad is…"

"Scotty Gibbons…we know." Says another leader.

I guess it is pretty obvious. "Ahem, will you excuse me?" I dart to the water fountain. I am feeling really lightheaded all of a sudden. Playing pastor's kid is going to be much different than at my old church where it seemed so natural. This entire culture is different. Not that I don't like it, I do, it is just unfamiliar. No one knows anything about who I am or where I have come from, and I am exhausted from having to explain my life story to every person I meet.

"Ah! There's my girl." A northern voice says behind me, cool and smooth like this icy water fountain.

"Tia? I was looking for you!"

"You were looking for me? I was looking for you. See that? We were double-looking. Ha! Woah, you're dressed nice. Are you liking school? Have you made any friends?"

"Really? Oh, thank you. Yes, I—"

"I was praying you would. I mean, praying for the right friends. Have you found any good friends, like actual ones you admire? Took *me* a second. Ha! More like a month."

"Um, sort of..." The word 'admire' makes me picture Mika McClain, not Carissa.

"Sort of? What do you mean, 'sort of'? You like, 'sort of' admire them? Oh, time for service." She yanks my arm, pulling me into a base-thumping auditorium with smoke and lights and rap music. The room is filled with teenagers—most of them boys who are much taller than me—in street style clothes. I do a little gulp. "Sit," she pats the seat next to her on the first row. "You'll love it here. You'll just love it."

"I already do," I smile, completely enthralled. A song is playing that I learned a hip hop dance to as a pre-teen, reminding me of the real Candice—or *Cassidy*, perhaps—who is very much expressive and (dare I say it) extroverted. It is like this new and wild side of me is emerging, like the cadence of a dancing cheerleader is running through my blood, an inner pulse to an Oklahoma City, athletic version of myself—the girl who has upperclassmen as friends and who might just become popular.

Chapter 6

CHOICES

"**C**HEER TRYOUTS ARE in the gym at 3:30 p.m. As previously stated, please remember to bring the completed paperwork required before coming to tryouts." Mrs. Gray's voice announces in 7th Hour. The classroom walls are plastered with Oklahoma State University track and field posters of ultra-muscular athletes supposed to motivate us track runners, along with everyone else who has Coach Stanley as their World History teacher. Today he is in a particularly rowdy mood, dealing off-colored jokes and human sacrifice stories to gore-hungry boys in the left corner of the classroom. I have brought along a plastic sack of dried blueberries and oatmeal squares to munch before track while considering the possibility of watching cheer tryouts, equally wondering if I should join them. "Coach, can you join both track and cheer?" I don't bother raising my hand. He is more likely to be offended if I do. I have learned the rules.

"You can join track cheerfully," he takes a kid's paper off his desk, looks over it uncaringly, folds it diagonally three times, and rips it into three even pieces. "Or die."

"I'm serious," I laugh, leaning over my desk. My hair is in messy curls and falling down my back—not as long as I want it to be, but longer than it has been since I was thirteen, and I am happy with it. I am wearing double stacked rings and two rope bracelets like the cheerleaders, dually sporting my track shirt and tennis shoes, feeling very much half-in, half-out of the two worlds. "I mean, I know they have similar practice times…"

"It's a free country." He unbuttons his top collar, running his fingers through his sweaty, curly white hair. "Ha! Every morning I wake up and look in the mirror and laugh. That reminds me, isn't every wrestler a Hindu?"

"Coach don't mind. Come to track when you can, go to cheer when you have to." Isaac Kennedy, the boy who looks like a wrestler, yells across the room, muttering in a lower voice, "But dunno know why anyone would wanna be a cheerleader."

"Cool, thanks." I lean back in my chair and cross my arms. Now that everything seems to be falling into place—school familiarity, popularity with the cheer girls, confidence in my homework—I think I am officially ready to join cheer. And I sense time is running out. If I do not make a move quickly, the popular girls may never ask me to go out to eat again—let alone invite me to a party. Remember, this is all part of my strategy: win everybody. Though I am not sure how well Keli will take the news that I have become a cheerleader, nor Isabelle, or anyone else for that matter. But who cares? Carissa is all that matters. If I can win her approval, I can do anything. Look out, world. Candice is about to become an OEH cheerleader.

"Hey, Carissa." I meet her at her locker at 3:02 p.m. She is wearing a spring-appropriate, skin-tight, lapis crop top and pearl choker, accentuating her blue eyes and Kendra Scott earrings.

She acts surprised, but not as surprised as I imagined. "Hey sugar," she surveys my hands, probably to ensure all my rings are stacked correctly.

"Soo…I heard cheer tryouts are today?"

She slams her locker with a dead-serious glare. "What, are you considering joining?"

Slightly offended, I play it safe. "Well, I was just thinking, you've been so nice to offer me a spot, and it would be fun to perform again, so, it wouldn't hurt to at least try out…"

She is not as impressed as I assumed.

"I mean, I'm not a gymnast, but I danced for several years."

"What kinds of dance?"

"Oh, pretty much everything—ballet, tap, jazz, lyrical, hip hop, clogging."

She studies my face, silently contemplating the pros and cons of Candice becoming a cheerleader. I am too. I can just imagine the Carissa Committee in her brain:

"She's already becoming popular with your friends. Might as well have her on your side."

"But look at her. She isn't like you!"

"But what if she turns the whole school against you?"

"Have you filled out the forms?" She probes, probably after this third thought.

"Oh, um, not yet."

Carissa bites her lip and looks left to right like we're about to elope. "Come with me." She grabs my arm, leading me up the enclosed staircase and down a green hallway as a short cut to the office. Is this exciting or what?!

Mrs. Gray is having her usual afternoon cup of coffee, and steam is fogging up her glasses. "What now, Carissa?" She signs absently. The office smells like caramel macchiato creamer, diluting the otherwise overpowering hospital disinfectant smell of sanitariness. It makes this feel more like home and less like the sterile penitentiary I toured prior to moving.

"You remember Candice Gibbons, the girl who shadowed me?"

Mrs. Gray peers at me disdainfully. How could she forget the girl with the low math grades who asked to switch her class schedule, who missed the bell more than once, and who doesn't check her school email regularly? Oh, yes. She knows me.

"She wants to join cheer."

"Has she completed the paperwork?"

"Well, not yet." Carissa shifts to her coaxing voice, leaning her weight to her left hip, and propping herself on the desk like a sales rep. "But I bet she could get it done at some point."

And naturally I would assume someone as sensible as Mrs. Gray would not fall for such a spill, but she does, and right now, I am thankful to have Carissa as a friend—whatever that means.

"So, you finally came to your senses?" Carissa blurts out loud enough for everyone to hear as we change clothes in the locker room. Her voice has changed back to its usual controlling tone. Since OEH is a relatively small school, the girls' locker room is shared by all the sports teams, and so the track girls are in here, too. And, until the upperclassmen enter, Carissa is the ruler of anyone who sets foot in this room. I have avoided the cheerleaders' corner until today due to the uncertainty of my status. I don't exactly feel accepted now, but since I walked in with Carissa, I figured I'd simply set my bag on the counter and dare myself not to overthink the situation.

I selectively choose my new Athleta shorts Gigi bought me, along with my OEH tee shirt from homecoming from my track bag. Even though the outfit is wrinkled, it is a neutral, casual, yet expensive look. "I didn't know you could join both track and cheer," I admit honestly, though of course that is not the real reason I waited nearly until March to announce I wanted to join the team.

"Can't wait to see what you've got!" Callie exclaims. She is wearing a pink Lululemon tennis skirt and is tightening her blond hair into a ponytail with double-stacked black hair ties.

Emma and Kinsley have entered and are looking at me like I have gone off the deep end, but they dare not say it to my face. Mika, on the other hand, walks towards me unafraid.

"You're trying out for cheer?"

"Yeah! First time!" I say happily.

"Yeah, well, that's cool! But, well, today's track practice is super important. I think Coach Lakyn is going to test us individually to see where we will be placed for the relay teams."

"Oh."

"Maybe you could tryout another time?" She turns to Carissa.

Carissa freezes combing her high ponytail. "Oh, um, I guess so." She switches to her well-mannered voice, flashing me a warning smile, like for some reason, this is going to blow my chance of properly joining cheer.

"You sure, Carissa? Would the cheer coach let me do that?"

"We have separate tryouts *all* the time." She vouches, eyeing Mika. "Totally works."

"Okay, if you're sure…"

"Great. Well, we were just about to head out to the gym. Are you ready? Do you want to walk with us?" Mika tells me.

So, here I am, walking disappointedly to a grueling workout of mountain climbers and push-up contests and speed circuits with girls who are actual athletes, while the tiny girls on the other side of the gym giggle and squeal and do all sorts of team building chants and stunts and pyramids. The curls in my hair have been shoved into a tangled, twisted ponytail, laughing at my neither athletic nor beautiful posture, as Candice's figure hangs under the bars of both athlete and cheerleader. My feet are already hurting from these drills. And hormonally, well, let's just say this could not have happened on a worse day.

"You're getting fast on these drills." Coach Lakyn encourages. "Alright, off your feet. Let's go into a core circuit." She bends down to talk into my ear. "Go into a plank."

Okay, I really like Coach Lakyn, but I really don't like planks. As in, I'd rather do pushups, sit-ups, reverse sit-ups—anything but this. She squats next to me. I am laying on the ground, stomach pulsing, head pulsing, heart pulsing—dying, really. Coach Lakyn is looking much nicer than the cheer coach on the other side of the gym yelling in girls' faces. I assume she is going to motivate me like those coaches do in the movies on the football fields, screaming into the stressed athletes' ears *"Don't quit!"* So, just like a real tired athlete who digs deep, I push myself to a plank position and breathe slow.

"I saw you signed up for the 400-meter dash. You know that is the hardest race of them all, right?"

Her words are not motivating. "No...why?" I stutter. This plank already hurts.

"It's the longest sprint. You have to maintain a fast pace for relatively the whole time. But there is a strategy."

Carissa...paperwork...I have to fill out paperwork...Carissa, Callie, Claire, Candice...My name starts with a C like theirs...

"Are you listening?"

No. My brain cannot compute her words from the echo of my pulse in my head.

Coach Lakyn snaps in my ear. "C'mon, Candice. I need you to stay present."

I blink back a storm of sweaty tears.

"Your first seven seconds are lightening—you give it all you've got. You know why?"

I don't care. I really don't care.

"Because your body can physically only run its hardest and fastest for about that long. At least, at the stage and place you are in. After that, you stride for about twenty seconds, leading you to the halfway point on the track."

Am I halfway through with this plank? Please, tell me I am.

"Settle yourself, Candice. You've got to settle into an easy, consistent pace. You will start to feel tired at the curve. This is the time you save energy so you can utilize it at the end of the race."

I squeeze my eyelids to keep sweat-infused makeup from dripping off my eyebrows and eyelashes into my eyes. I am not an athlete. I never was and never will be. Why am I saying this? Okonkwo would finish the plank. Did they even have planks in Iguedo? Planks of wood, probably. Not this kind. I feel like a piece of wood Carissa is bouncing on to snap.

"And finally, when you come around the corner, you build momentum, passing the weakest girls and building up speed. This is where the real athletes emerge."

Breathe deep, Candice. Breathe deep.

"This is where you hold nothing back."

This is all I have left in me.

"For the remaining distance, you give it everything you got."

"Got...it."

Drops of sweat trickle to the waxed basketball court floor. My core muscles are shaking like a rattling smoothie blender.

I finally collapse.

I think I could handle my first ice bath right now.

"You just did your longest plank time." She checks her watch.

"Real...ly?"

"Candice, you are stronger than you think you are."

"Thanks,"

"No, I mean it." She helps me up. "And those girls over there? You have potential not just to look pretty, but to be a strong leader. Track is pulling that out of you. I can see it. I'm glad you're on the team."

"Thanks, Coach. Me too." I smile wearily.

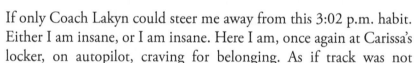

If only Coach Lakyn could steer me away from this 3:02 p.m. habit. Either I am insane, or I am insane. Here I am, once again at Carissa's locker, on autopilot, craving for belonging. As if track was not enough. As if I am still Carissa's shadow.

"Can we help you?" Callie speaks up. Carissa won't make eye contact.

"I wanted to see when I could do my cheer tryout."

Both blonds exchange glances.

"*There* you are!" Keli says a few feet behind me. Her timing could not be any worse.

I turn ever so slightly, trying to maintain eye contact with the cheerleaders.

"Coach Stanley is looking for you." Keli grabs my hand.

Carissa smirks. "Better go, then, honey."

This is just great.

"Here we read about the changes Okonkwo undergoes in relation to his cultural surroundings. There is tension, resistance, anarchy, and…Keli, do you have a problem?"

"Ahhh," she yawns. "No, ma'am. It just…it all sounds so familiar. Know what I mean?"

"Iguedo is OEH, that's what." Kenny says. The class snickers, minus a few popular kids in the back with their tiny noses shielded behind creaseless novels.

"Now, that brings up a good point. How do we see change—whether communal or individual—affecting our lives? Hmm? Who has ever had a big change before?"

Oh, this applies to me. I raise to a normal posture height in my uncomfortable desk. I was fading.

"I lost my grandpa last summer," says a tan girl passively. "But he left us with a condo in Hawaii, so it all worked out."

"I woke up to a new car one day," says a blond boy with big teeth and bad breath. "It's like our ninth—or is it our tenth? I forget. We're building a new garage unit right now. My dad likes trading exotic cars. It's a side hobby. Oh, but those rims, though! Man, can't wait 'till I'm sixteen. Bro!"

"When I moved here it was a change," I start to say quietly. Only a small girl with a forlorn face and a purple fuzzy jacket listens behind me. She looks like her name would start with an M, like Mariah or Mary. "Moving from Missouri was a very big change." I add, but that is as far as I get in my sad tale because Mrs. Abernathy just realized what an awful question that was to ask a class of hungry, rich sophomores, and Okonkwo is waiting on us in chapter five.

"I'm getting a *what?*"

"Mr. Groath emailed last night suggesting a nice, retired teacher named Amy Kim for out-of-school math tutoring." Mom says.

Unbelievable. This is exactly what I needed right now. Just when I thought I was going to make it with the sharks at OEH, here I am sinking. We are standing at Mom's bathroom sink, lined with several family members' toothbrushes and hair supplies. Mom and Dad's bathroom is the catch-all for clothes, boxes, dolls, dinosaurs—you name it. It kind of symbolizes the chaos of our lives in this season of sacrifice. "Tutoring is for delinquents! Dumb kids! *Losers!*" I follow her into the closet where she has started folding laundry. "Mom, you've got to understand. You were a teenager…once."

She laughs in a not-buying-it sort of tone.

"Mom, Mother, *Marmee,* I'm already struggling to be associated with the cheerleaders ever since the Galantine's dinner. And I thought you said I should try to reach everyone. You know, be nice to all the cliques. The *last* thing I need is another hit to my social life."

"You're right. You should reach everyone. But there is more to life than being popular. Besides, your grades come first."

"Of course, I know that." I answer, "But God called me to influence this school. How can I influence anyone if I don't have any friends?" I help her fold a fuzzy blanket that has lost its actual fuzz in the dryer and now resembles a staticky square of that stuff you crinkle in animal cages. Our whole life feels like an animal cage.

Mom does not answer me right away, giving me time to consider the doubts I have had about moving. "Maybe I'm not supposed to be at OEH…" I say slowly.

"Hmph! Maybe we aren't supposed to be here at all." Mom mutters.

That was weird. This is one of the first times I have heard Mom doubt God's plan for our lives—like maybe we interpreted the prophecies wrong. And truth is, I can't disagree with her. *Everything's* going wrong. "What is done is done," she says after a long pause, and we walk back into the bathroom. "Canzie, you've got to keep your grades up if you want to run track. Mark your calendar. Mrs. Kim is planning to meet you at Braum's Ice Cream every other day after school. It starts tomorrow. *No arguing about this one!*" she says, redoing her blond ponytail.

"*Braum's?!*" I explode. "That's where, like, every kid who lives on the east side of town goes after school! Like, I know several kids that go there. Ugh! Now everyone's going to know I have a tutor!" I slump down against the bathtub and moan. It's like God keeps making my life worse and worse. *What did I do to deserve this?*

Fresh off the track, I walk into Braum's towards my doom.

"Are you *Kansas?*" An older Asian woman approaches me carrying a white knitted purse.

I shift the weight of my backpack and wipe sweat from my forehead. I am grossly sticky and highly aware my legs are going to stick to the booth bench and leave a puddle of sweat. The only good news is I think I got a little sunburned today, which means a tan is on its way. Still, it is not enough to cheer me up from this prospect. Nothing can. "It's Candice, and I'm afraid so." I quickly scan the room for any OEH faces. So far, so good.

Mrs. Kim laughs and points to a side booth. "Sit here. We will look at your math and help you understand." I shrug and pull out my math homework. *Yes, please do help me find the right answers.*

Chapter 7

QUESTIONS

G OING TO SCHOOL is *not* as magical as I originally imagined. I used to think it was as easy as saluting to your friends in the hall, slamming a locker, and effortlessly enjoying the athlete life. But of course, it's not. 'Torn' does not begin to describe the anxiety I feel over losing favor with the cheerleaders. But was I even supposed to seek it in the first place? Who knows. Honestly, having friends *at all* is nearly impossible. One wrong move and you are quickly written off as "one of them." If I ride with the popular girls, I get sour looks from the average kids who know the cheerleaders are two-faced drama queens. And while I am with the cheerleaders, even if they acknowledge me once every thousand years, I am still a third wheel. But I don't even fit in with the misfits who live the alternative lifestyle. Really, the average kids are almost the hardest, glued to their circles of secluded friends, while I aspire to be a confident, socially aware sophomore with respectable friends and a good appearance.

Complicated? That's one way to put it, and let's not get started on having a math tutor for a class I am already enrolled in for the grade below me. It makes sense why I am not as confident as I was when I first became an OEH student. I am realizing just how little I know about pop culture, fashion trends, and clique cues. I don't own a single thing brand-worthy to be called "rich." I am barely considered a track runner because of my feet problems—I can scarcely run the warm-up laps. And as fun as journalism is—the one thing I am remotely good at—it definitely does not help my social circle. Being in Journalism is the equivalent of being the robotics club, or something equally unpopular, and its appeal is small aside from Mrs. Lajuana's appreciated companionship.

Now that we have officially moved, reality is sinking in. I miss having friend access. You can only FaceTime your best friends so many times. I miss crashing at my grandparents' farm in Missouri and spending nights at Annie's house on weekends. Instead, I am stuck in this city neighborhood where we park on a steep driveway and can smell our neighbor's food and watch them eat it with their TV show just by looking out the window. I can't stand sharing a room, closet, and bathroom. I know I sound selfish and spoiled. I am. But right now, I am in survival mode: I wake up, get dressed, leave for school in the dark of the morning, endure a cruel day of walking class to class by myself, face the winter wind on my way to the cafeteria (I haven't been asked to go out to lunch in ages), nearly pass out at track practice, finish two hours of homework after dinner, and then shuffle into bed like a robot. I am supposed to "step out in faith" and "enjoy this new season of adventure," but instead I feel gloomy, isolated, and purposeless.

It is March now, and not one of the popular girls have done so much as smile at me. It hurts the most on Friday's when I spot Morgan, Afton, and Carey riding off to lunch totally ignoring me and forcing me to walk to the cafeteria building with the freshmen *who have friends.* Even if the cheerleaders did end up eating in the cafeteria, I do not think I would be welcomed at the popular table. Not since Keli has stuck beside me like glue and track season has started. It is like the cheerleaders' think I have joined the drug crowd and sealed my fate.

Lately, I have been sitting with Mabrey and Isabelle at the socially awkward average kids' table because it is literally the only place I can go without having to sit at the druggie table. And some days, just to shake things up, I do choose to sit beside Keli and endure uncomfortable conversations about inappropriate topics while looking highly interested in my signature lunch of mini ham and cheese cubes. I like changing tables because it keeps everyone guessing on who I am with, which helps me not be one hundred percent categorized as a goth girl, cheerleader recruit, or average kid with no purpose, even if it does make me a floater. I am Candice Gibbons, for crying out loud. I am supposed to reach everyone.

But who is the *real* Candice? Is she a formerly homeschooled Missourian, stuck in her past life? Is she just a quirky journalism student or a wannabe track star? Is she a cheerleader named Cassidy who has totally gone off the deep end into American pop culture? No, I have definitely not fallen that far…yet. Don't forget, I gave my life *completely* to God when we moved here. I have been studying the life of Jesus. He hung out with the misfits and was kind to everyone. And so far, that pretty much sums up my social life.

But what about the attention I am getting from the cheerleaders; how they want me to join their little clique? It is like I am on a teeter-totter. Every day I either move a step closer to popularity or a step towards becoming an outcast, and as a result, I have worked up resentment from both sides. Am I doing something wrong?

"Why did you sit with *them* yesterday?" Isabelle asked me the other day, alluding to the popular table.

"I dunno. It's not like there are assigned seats or anything," I surveyed the drama kids at our table with dangling earbud wires reading sci-fi books. This is the most demographically integrated table in the cafeteria. Maybe it is because kids are accepted for who they are, and nobody bothers them. Well, unless you're a *popular girl*, which apparently, I am in their eyes.

"I am not!" I said with eager emphasis when Isabelle muttered I was a wannabe cheerleader trying to be like Carissa. I did not mean for my voice to come out so strong, it just happened automatically. Then Isabelle gaped at me like she didn't think my voice could ever sound so strong. The real Candice emerged. The real, struggling Candice.

"Then why do you hang out with *them?*" Mabrey uncharacteristically piped in. Two boys emerged from their sci-fi novels, eager to hear my response.

"Look, I just moved here. I am not stuck in one circle. I've sat at that table over there," I point at Keli, who salutes back. "And, well, I've sat at Carissa's table too. So what?"

"So, you're a floater," a girl with wiry glasses pointed out. I pondered her words and hesitated to respond.

"I guess I am," I finally chuckled confidently.

Yet, on the inside, I felt anything but secure in my identity.

Last night was a weird dream: Diana and I rode mules to school, where I was asked to do a podcast about OEH. Then Carissa showed up and handed me a glittery cheer uniform with the word STANLEY in sparkly letters, but I told her Sophia and I were going to the pool. It ended in a messy street fight with me against the druggies. The druggies won.

I roll around in bed a few minutes before remembering it is the second day of spring break. Spring break meant nothing to me in Missouri because we did not really get a break. But now, as a private schooler, it is like a whiff of sweet roses. The world is finally blossoming out of winter, and I can feel it. Yesterday, I painted encouraging quotes on scraps of wood while listening to acoustic worship. I don't even gravitate toward music with guitars, and I am not exactly an artist. It was so uncharacteristic of me, yet subtly comforting. Not picturesque; sitting on the porch overlooking dead grass and a bare fence while trying to paint in the wind and straining to hear the music above traffic horns, but still relaxing. I forgot how much I enjoyed time alone outside, reflecting, praying, contemplating. Life felt less gray then.

But now I am back to reality. I am living in a random rental house in a random neighborhood in a random city in a random state. Today is supposed to be a cloudy Tuesday and there will be nothing exciting to do because it will be too cold or windy to be outside.

Moving definitely feels like a mistake.

"Canzie?" Mom creaks open the bedroom door. We have not spoken to each other in who knows how long, and when we do, our conversations are tense.

"Morning." I roll over.

"Want to have a girl's day together?" She says in her sweet voice—the voice of my childhood. When I do not respond right away, she adds in a pitiful voice, "I thought we could use some time to be together, since we haven't been on great terms..."

I sit up on bed and rub my eyes, barely comprehending her words. "Yeah. Sure."

"Great! I'm ready whenever you are." She closes the door.

Once I realize what I have agreed to, I hop out of bed and actually smile for the first time in what feels like an eternity. I decide on my cream sweater with my suede lacy shoes. I try my best to poof up my half-wavy, half-straight mess of hair with some hairspray. I think this is the first time I have left this house for something fun. This will be good. We will go somewhere and do something unrelated to school or tutoring or track.

Around 10:00 a.m., we hop in the car and drive to a nail salon by my request. If there is one thing every single decent OEH student has from the 'averages' up, it is manicured nails. So obviously, I am going to jump at Mom's generosity to bless me.

When we walk in, there is country music in the background and a toxic stench of nail polish remover. It is not too crowded, which means there is less of a chance I will spot any OEH spies. My poor, track-worn feet begin to relax as they soak in the pedicure jacuzzi tub.

"This is going to be a fun girls' day," Mom says.

"Yeah, thanks for doing this." I smile, not allowing myself to miss the moment because of my own anxiety over cheer or worries about the track meet coming up. I am determined to enjoy today. The more I sit in these massage chairs and my toes are soothed and clipped and painted, the more I feel like my old self. There aren't any OEH students—I keep checking just to make sure—and it gives me an unusual relief that I can revert to the *true* Candice.

I lean my head against the back of the massage chair. "Oh, Mom. I feel so drained after every single day of school."

"Don't you like OEH?"

"Some days better than others."

"What makes it hard?"

"Not having any friends. Not wanting to mess up. Not knowing where I fit in, mainly."

"But I thought you said you were meeting some new friends,"

"More like *acquaintances*. I wouldn't invite a single girl over to hangout. Everyone has their own friend group." And now I am caught off guard by the lyrics to the country song currently playing called *I'm Going Home*. It makes me think of the Bricks, of our little yellow cottage, and all the fuzzy feelings being loved, accepted, and valued. "It's like everyone fits in a friend group—even the socially awkward kids! And while I'm trying to "be an influence" and "be a light," how much can you really influence a group of complacent Christian rich kids?"

"Maybe things will be different after spring break. Maybe they're still getting used to you. Maybe *they* don't know where you'll fit in, I mean, you're a track kid who makes journalism videos. Perhaps they're still figuring out if it's safe to be friends with you.

"Safe? Like I'm some kind of threat? I feel like a little fly swarming around a den of lions. I feel invisibly purposeless. Even at track."

"Oh, that's right. You enjoy track, don't you? Why don't you make friends with your teammates?"

"Yeah right…" I shudder, picturing their reactions if I asked to be friends. "I hardly get a 'hey' when we start with warm-up laps, Mom. It doesn't help they're mostly juniors and seniors, I have *zero* classes with them…not to mention I am the slowest runner on the team."

We hobble our wet toes to the manicure stand and choose a French.

"How is tutoring?" Mom says loud enough for everyone to hear us.

"Fine." I lower my voice drastically to hopefully clue her in.

"Are you learning?"

"Yes."

"How are your grades?"

"The same."

"What? Why?!"

"Because I have only gone once to tutoring, and we have not done any big tests since then. At least I am not going backwards!" I whisper annoyedly.

"Let's get some ice cream after this." Mom shakes her head wearily, and I immediately bite my tongue. I have not had ice cream in weeks due to track, and I do not want to feel guilty all week long. But "Why not," I say, before my conscience interferes.

Mom has been so gentle, so patient, and I feel sort of guilty for being a drag these past few months. I can't begin to express how thankful I am for her kindness.

After we eat our ice cream, we drive to a movie theater inside a mall and watch a mystery that has us clutching each other's arms. I am more of a mystery-watcher than Mom, so I am excited she even volunteered to watch this with me. Frankly, it feels like I am squeezing my best friend's arm and not my mom's. Maybe it is because she is the only friend I have right now.

When the credits roll, we stop by the food court, grab some chow mein and bourbon chicken and talk about the movie. Ironically, the movie began with a girl moving to a new town struggling to fit in. She makes a few mistakes, like causing trouble in the school, but by the end of the movie she has an team of misfit girls from different crowds—a science nerd, a drama kid, and a popular girl. If only life were that easy. "There are definitely kids that fit all of those stereotypes at OEH," I inform Mom, twisting noodles around my chopsticks.

"Maybe God will use you as middle ground between all of the cliques." Mom pours soy sauce over her chicken. "Like the girl did in the movie."

"Maybe," I mutter halfheartedly. *You should just drop out.* A negative thought whispers. I feel a fist of worms in my stomach, like these noodles here. "Or maybe I'm not supposed to be at OEH at all."

"*I* know you're supposed to be there." Mom assures. I know it is true, seeing how God brought our family here and all. That is, *if*

75

He really did. What if we got it all wrong? It is so hard to grasp why I don't feel like I have a purpose at school.

As we walk outside in the sunlight, I scrutinize my shiny nails. Now I look a little more like the girls at OEH with my nails done... that's got to help something. "Thanks for doing this," I say to Mom on the drive home. "I really needed it."

"I did too," she says. "I've really been missing you lately."

"You can always pick me up for lunch."

"Really? They'd let me do that?"

"Of course. A ton of kids with cars leave campus for lunch. I just sit by myself."

"I thought you ate with Carissa..."

"That was on the day I shadowed her. She goes out to eat with her friends."

"Even though sophomores aren't allowed to eat out?"

"Carissa Carlyle rides above the law."

"Ha! You act like she's a notorious criminal, Canzie!"

"Yeah—that or an evil spy. Every encounter alters her language, Mom. She literally—literally—changes voice inflections depending on her surroundings. Her hands obnoxiously display glittery sequences of double-stacked rings and her striking blue eyes flash with a serpent's intuition." I push up my eyelids with my fingers in exaggeration. "Her scarlet lips slit a wicked grin like she knows something about the universe—about *me*. She is like a lioness bored of a squeamish ant. Dropping her chin, it is as if she intuitively follows some invisible code of mannerisms." I shake off a chill. "Now that I think about it," I lean over the table and drop to a whispered tone of helpless regret, "she might *be* a criminal, Mom."

"Oh, my word. All this drama. You're reading into this too much. She's just a sixteen-year-old girl like you. I bet she even has a nice family. Maybe I can reach out to her mom..."

"NO!" I choke on my noodles. "No way. I bet her mom is a version of her times two. Who knows? Please don't, that would make things worse."

"Alright, alright. Sheesh, no need to panic. *You're* probably the weird one in this situation being all standoffish and introverted. You know you are a bit awkward, Canzie. Why don't you just ask to ride with her to lunch the next time you see her?"

"Mom! You can't just invite yourself to join a clique!" I blurt back, blocking out the image of asking for a ride from Carissa like I am one of her hopeless admirers.

"But I thought they liked you! Didn't you get invited to their Valentine's dinner?"

"Yeah, they 'like me.' I think it has something to do with their boyfriends. Or to get me to join cheer." I roll my eyes.

"Why don't you join cheer? What's wrong with that?"

"I don't know. *Ugh...I don't know what I want anymore!*" I explode.

Not a great way to end this day.

"Young journalist, since you missed picture day last semester, you'll need to go have yours retaken during our class hour tomorrow. Don't worry, you won't get penalized. Just go get your picture taken in the chapel building." Mrs. Lajuana tells me in second hour.

"Oh, like for the yearbook?" I light up. "Cool!" Here is something fun to add to my monotonous schedule—my first time having a real yearbook picture! Throughout class I can't help but plan out the perfect hair and outfit combo. Curled hair? Most definitely. Choker? Absolutely. *I can't wait for tomorrow!*

"Your hair looks nice today!" Mika twirls one of my curls on my way out the door to get my picture taken during class.

My hair did turn out nicely—even a little Mika-ish—with all my curls. "Thank you, Mika!"

"It does look nice," says her boyfriend generously, holding the mic that is about to be hooked to her shirt. "So, you're gonna miss this newscast?"

"Yeah, but I'll be back as soon as I can."

As I walk by myself out the school doors and across campus to the chapel, I feel a cool breeze on my shoulders. Shivering in my short sleeve shirt, I quicken my pace when I notice clouds suddenly cover the sky.

And then the worst happens.

I am immersed in a *downpour*—literal downpour—of thundering rain. I try to run in my sandals, and it splashes puddles of water on my jeans. *Please no…please no…please no…* I throw my backpack over my head like an umbrella to guard my curls.

It is too late. By the time I reach the chapel building and run up to the picture lady, I am a soaking mess.

"Oh, darlin', what *happened* to you?" The astonished photographer tilts her head to the side trying to see the best in me.

"It…started…to…storm…" I huff and puff. Excusing myself to the bathroom, I squeeze out water from my hair and try my best not to allow tears to join the rain on my face. Apparently, God is trying to cure me from vanity or something. Or just humiliating me for being gullible enough to move here after some random vision.

"You're up," the photographer peaks her head in the bathroom. And so, I shake my wet mane of hair and march to the folding chair, smile as best as I can despite feeling soaked in monotony and unpopularity. *So much for my first yearbook picture.*

"Sorry about that," Mom says unsympathetically with a hint of bitterness in her voice.

It feels like I have a permanent home on this OEH sidewalk. "It's just frustrating having to sit on the curb in the school parking lot for an *hour* after practice. Picture me standing here every day with my heavy backpack and track bag in the freezing cold while all of my teammates drive by in their luxury cars. It's not only inconvenient, it's humiliating!" I throw my backpack on the floor. It is weighty with math worksheets. Dozens. My head is throbbing in my ears, and I feel like I am catching pneumonia or something. But then I notice Mom's face is red and she has tearstains on her cheeks, and as much as I am tempted to focus on myself and my own problems, I would be heartless not asking her if she is okay.

"No, I'm not." She hisses, swerving out of the lot.

I bite my tongue to keep from saying "me neither." This is about her, not me. "Care to share?" I say in a meek voice.

"Moving is hard!" Mom says in a laugh that sounds more like an inner cry for help. "I've been driving like a madwoman nonstop between all of the family's schools and activities. This is insane!" She speeds down the highway.

I guess we are in the same boat: the same, sinking boat.

Here's to Day Three of being picked up late from track practice repeatedly. Mom remains silent for most of the way home, but I barely notice. I have had too much school drama to hear anyone else's problems. This is not how I should be, but it is reality. Keli and her boyfriend broke up today, and you would think I was her personal counselor. Mr. Groath went off on the class and gave us a hundred math problems to do by the weekend, which is more terrifying to me than sitting by myself in the cafeteria…though I can add that to this week's accomplishments.

"In case you were wondering, I was at the eye doctor." Mom breaks the silence.

"Why couldn't…Dad pick me up?" I cough.

"He's in meetings at the church until six." She cuts back quickly. "The world doesn't revolve around you, you know."

I have been feeling that more and more. I don't fit in at my cliquish school, on the track, or even in my diverse youth group. I don't have a single friend or mentor. Even Keli won't acknowledge me unless she needs something, and then she's off with her new and less improved friend circle. And of course, there's academics. There is so much homework I am constantly drowning in assignments due. I can't remember the last time I spent the 9:00 p.m. hour not cramming to finish homework. This is big for a girl who likes to retire at 8:00 p.m. Oh, and this isn't including the pressure I feel from Mr.

Groath to keep my math grades up. Thanks to him, I am on my way to tutoring so I can keep up with the freshmen level math homework. When I think about all these things, it makes sense to doubt if this was truly God's calling for my life.

"We're leaving fifteen minutes early so we can stop and get coffee," Kelly tells me just five minutes before our new departure time. I have been looking forward to Friday all week. Not only does it mean launching the end of the week, but it is Chapel Day, so classes are shorter, lunch break is longer, and I get to switch up my mundane school routine to walk to the chapel building. Plus, everyone is required to dress up. I am in the middle of curling my hair, which is going to look perfect with my silky gray shirt and black skirt. I even decide on a pair of heels, just because I can. I am excited to show up in something other than a sweatshirt for a change. Let's just hope it does not rain.

Before I know it, it is time to leave, and I forgot that I was supposed to iron my black skirt. Now I have to decide whether to wear it wrinkled or just go with jeans. I zip it on and examine myself in the mirror. Nope, too wrinkled. Mom always taught me wrinkles are a statement of sloppiness. I throw on my rip-free blue jeans and run out the door. Nothing to be concerned about.

Sitting in Journalism class, I am complimenting Mika's navy-blue dress when all of a sudden, it hits me. My face turns red. I swallow a giant gulp. I notice a common trend around the room. I can't believe I messed up this bad. I forgot the big rule against wearing jeans on Chapel Day.

Oh, great! I have heard kids getting in trouble for this all the time. And here I am—proudly sporting my denim pants like it is any day but chapel day. If there is ever a moment to be invisible, it is now.

"M-Mrs. Lajuana, may I please call my mom? I forgot something," I whisper at her desk.

"Is it important?"

"Yes ma'am, *very,*"

Harper the sloppy junior, who actually fixed her hair today, taps me on the shoulder. "The newscast is ready to be filmed. We need you on the set."

I look past her and see Mika miking up ready to lead the broadcast.

"*Please,* I'll be really quick!" I beg Mrs. Lajuana, feeling as though everyone knows about my dress code violation but me, that everyone is waiting on me to fix it. What, do they think I am about to broadcast this mistake to the entire school?

Thankfully Mrs. Lajuana consents, and I hurriedly call Mom and ask her to bring my black pants, hoping I am not on her bad side.

But what if she says no?!

"We're definitely missing the newscast right now," Harper complains, trailing behind me on our way to the office. Mrs. Lajuana made Harper join me to make sure I stayed on course and did not get lost. I guess she still considers me a liability ever since I lost my way on Alien Day. I don't blame her, but now this is really awkward, and Harper, the sloppy junior, couldn't be more ticked off.

Thank goodness Mom said she would bring me some black pants. I know I don't deserve her kindness. I've been so high maintenance lately. "Thank you *so much!*" I say to Mom at the car window. Mom hands me my pants, still confused over the whole situation. I didn't bother telling her I was violating dress code; there wasn't time nor clearance. Thankfully, she is in a rush to take my sister Allison to her new dance studio, so I just wave to her and run inside where Harper is holding the door for me. "Next stop, bathroom."

Harper eyes me suspiciously. "Your big emergency was you needed black pants?"

I shrug my shoulders and flash a sheepish grin.

"My life's a lie," she throws up her hands. "Myyyyy life's a lie."

"I totally blanked when I threw on my blue jeans today. I forgot about the chapel dress code." I say, walking in a stall. "You mean you never knew?"

"I could've sworn you were wearing dark navy slacks."

"Nope," I untie my shoes. I have never been more excited to get out of my comfy jeans and stretch into the itchiest pair of slacks I own. It is glorious to be in uniform.

"So, I missed being an announcer in my first newscast so you could color coordinate your chapel outfit?"

"Oh, Harper! I'm so sorry. I didn't know you were *in* this newscast!"

"Well, why do you think I did my hair today?" Harper retorts. I hear her sigh and wash her hands out of boredom. *No wonder people don't want to be friends with me—I am so inconsiderate.* "Thanks for coming," I say gently. "Sorry you had to, I mean."

Harper is quiet for a moment, probably deciding if she ever wants to talk to me again. "You have the nicest mom ever," she finally says.

"What?"

"I mean, my mom would *never* leave what she was doing to bring me something. You must have a pretty cool family."

"Yeah, I guess so." I mutter. But honestly, I feel anything *but* close to my family.

"Can you guys be *quiet?*" I fume, earnestly trying to finish my homework before Mr. Groath's wrath rains down on my life. Here's to my one billionth hour crouched over homework at the sticky kitchen table in the space that serves as the living room, kitchen, dining room, Candice's vanity stand, and now, my homework table. Someone might as well shove me underwater because I am already drowning in this rental house.

Jordan is smacking goldfish to my left, Angel is painting her nails while eating a dripping grape popsicle, not to mention listening to music, and Bria and Allison are playing Chinese Checkers in front of me. If this isn't the perfect recipe for distraction, I don't know what is.

"Want Nemo?" Jordan offers me a soggy piece of goldfish in my face.

It falls in my lap. Charlie eats it.

"La, la, la la…" Angel sings even louder.

"It's your move!"

"No, it's your turn!" Bria and Allison argue.

"Hey Candice, can you review my English paper?" Kelly walks up and asks.

"Where's Mom?" Angel yells over the music.

"She is crying in her closet," Bria says.

"What's wrong with her?" I interject, yanking out an earplug (though I am not listening to anything, it is merely to divert attention away from my presence).

"She is working through moving to Oklahoma." Dad zooms past the table with a phone to his ear.

Of course, she is. It has become mutually understood how moving has produced a broad range of emotional reactions. To show how chaotic it is at our rental house, OEH feels like a beautiful escape… and of course, everyone knows how I feel about OEH. At least I can vent out my anger on the track. Not like running until I pass out is my top choice for coping, but desperate times require desperate measures. *Oh, this season of sacrifice!*

"Are you settling in your new house?" Tia asks me after youth group.

"Haha," I zip up my jacket before walking outside to the wind of Oklahoma. Should I tell Tia we're just trying to survive the next four months while they build our actual house? No, too much detail. I expect her to shake my hand and say she will be praying for me, but instead she leaves her post as a door greeter and follows me to Big Roy rattling in the sunset.

"Moving is hard. There is no way around it."

"Tell me about it," I mutter.

"Well, if you ever need anything, here's my number." She rips off a corner of her notebook with a '405' area code and phone number on it.

"Wow, ugh, thanks." Just knowing I have one Oklahoma person who knows as much as my name and that I am a Christian, someone who isn't trying to recruit me for cheer or give me drugs, this is a surprise. It is strange how one small act of kindness can impact someone so much. I like the culture of my new church. I like Tia. "I wish you could come with me to school tomorrow," I chuckle quietly, feeling so depleted and fatigued and lightheaded.

"Hey, girl, hey," she punches me in the arm like we have been friends for years. She almost reminds me of my friend, Sophia. "You're a world-changer on your own, girl. Go turn it upside down for Jesus!"

But why does everyone see "world-changer" in me but me?

What exactly makes them think that?

Chapter 8

CASSIDY

M Y HANDS ARE trembling with chills as I once again enter the double doors to New Life Church, but it is probably just nerves, though I do have a slight cough and my eyes are red and hollow like faded bruises. I look seriously depleted. I *feel* depleted. But it is not like I can do anything about it. This is survival mode. I have to be strong or else I will lose everything—traction on the track, clout with the cheerleaders, promotions in Journalism, biology aggression, passing math grades—all the pressures I feel like I cannot tell anyone about; the pressure I have because otherwise I will be medicated or taken out of school or who knows what else. Yes, I must stay calm and act normal. I was made for this...I think.

Whatever. I do not have the energy to think deep thoughts. Hopefully no one notices this tall, struggling sixteen-year-old parked in the back of the auditorium. When I told to my friend Jaclyn about New Life, I described it as warm, friendly, and free-spirited: *"The smell of coffee greets you at the doors. The diversity combined with unity makes the entire church radiate with enthusiastic acceptance. I really do love the genuine interest in people everyone expresses."* Yet, even if this place was a new version of Disney World, it would still unfamiliar. And unfamiliar places can seem as foreign as living on another planet, regardless the benefits. I texted Tia to see if she would be here, but she is sick this week. Figures. My eyes scan the room for anyone familiar. But no; everyone either already has friends or looks disinterested to meet me. I can't blame them. My hair hasn't been washed in days, and I am wearing an oversized wrinkly white tee shirt with the comical words 'We Over Me' in the center, and black jeans with holes in the knees. I think I still have my track tennis shoes on. Yeah, I do.

My sisters, Kelly and Bria, have found front row seats beside Joshua and Jeremiah Jackson, and while they are fun to be around, I need somewhere quiet and secluded where I can talk to God without an entire church congregation watching me. As worship begins and ends, I realize I never uttered a single word. Everyone worshipped so freely—jumping, clapping, shouting. But Candice the PK, who is usually worshipping at the altar beside Jaclyn lifting her hands and singing, is the back aisle, head down. Her heart is angry, frustrated, and confused why this is the outcome of moving after she offered God such sacrificial obedience. She's back to unidimensional Cassidy. This is the last stage.

I changed my entire life for you. I grip the seat in front of me and clench my teeth. *You couldn't send me one friend, one decent schoolmate, not even some skills to run track?* I feel so dumb, but I am almost waiting on that supernatural wind that came last summer when I visited the church in Alabama to blow my hair. I am waiting on that still, inaudible voice to tell me how everything is going to work out. But it doesn't come.

I do not know how long I can play "happy Candice" at school, church, or even at our rental house. If God is not speaking to me like He did on my trip to Alabama, how can I be close to Him? And what if God never spoke to me in the first place?!

Perhaps it was not really a supernatural voice that said, "go to Oklahoma" but my own wild imagination. Perhaps Dad heard wrongly about the direction of our family. I have always been a born and raised Missouri girl, and the fact that Missouri has become more and more appealing upon moving here, well, it looks pretty obvious. What if these horrible Oklahoma outcomes are God's way of punishing me for stepping outside of His will for my life?

Maybe moving was a mistake.

"Good practice today, girls. Make sure to stretch those hamstrings and drink some chocolate milk when you get home. Our first track meet is right around the corner." Coach Stanley tells us while we limp over to our water bottles after a grueling endurance drill called "the ladder."

"Let's see," says Emma the junior, reading scribbled words the palm of her hand. "Tonight, I've got a hot date."

"Who has a hot date?" Coach Stanley picks up on Emma's words.

"Kidding, Coach." Emma rolls her eyes. "I've got a hot date with the series I am streaming. Tonight is the final episode."

Kinsley laughs and reads what is on her hand. "Look, Coach. I've got one two...with my Ben and Jerry's Half-Baked and a Lit paper,"

I peek at my hand out of impulse and, to my surprise, find a few words I had scribbled down in World History. I have the word "college" spelled out, because it is literally my goal to survive this horrible sophomore year and move back to Missouri to attend my dream university. Moreover, I am seriously looking ahead—even past this whole moving drama. What kind of person do I want to be? How are today's decisions going to affect future Candice?

It is not too early to consider my life direction. There are more meaningful ways to spend my thoughts and time than binging on ice cream and streaming a series. Like, those things are fun, and this time last year I would have probably been right there with Emma and Kinsley, but things have changed. Sometimes it takes a minor crisis to wake you up from comfort and complacency. Especially with these new contact lenses, I feel so vulnerable and real.

It all sounds mature of me, but that is not entirely what I am processing. To complicate things, I still feel increasingly inexistent. I do not feel as motivated to succeed in *anything*. I am just too tired to keep self-motivating myself to succeed. "See ya," everyone calls, quickly vanishing off the track, but I am planning on spending as much time as possible untying my track spikes, because I know for a fact Mom is going to be late picking me up.

"You okay?" Mika's voice says behind me. I wipe sweat off my forehead with my hand and turn around. Not even a confident senior can cheer me up at a time like this. Still, it feels nice to have someone talk to me directly today. First one.

"Just tired."

"Me too," she runs her fingers through her sweaty curls. "Being a senior has its struggles."

"I can only imagine." I play with the end of my ponytail. Mika stretches her legs and sighs, probably feeling obliged to stay and talk to me. *Just go home in your cute white Jeep.* I inwardly think, though I know I don't mean it. It is nice not being left alone with my own thoughts. I glance up at her face and smile. "You're a really great long-distance runner, Mika."

"Not good enough."

I stare at her perplexed. This girl has everything—looks, talent, popularity—yet she feels like she doesn't measure up. How sad is that?

"There's always someone better. Some girl, somewhere, with a better PR. Y'know? Well, I better run...er, I mean go," she laughs, throwing her drawstring bag over her shoulder. "See ya around."

"Yeah. See ya."

I still can't believe Mika McClain is insecure. I mean, I guess everyone has insecurities, but I never thought *she* would. Well, there's another sad fact about life. People aren't perfect. We are all failing. I say goodbye to Coach Stanley and start to leave when he pulls my arm.

"Why are you running track if it's obvious you aren't a runner?"

I am not offended. People can say what they want. "I wanted to prove to myself I could do something hard." I am in the subconscious, which can be dangerously more real than the conscious.

"Hard is right," he laughs. "So, what's your definition of victory?"

"Running my first track meet." I state. "Being the real deal."

"Explain yourself." He lowers the height of several white hurdles with the red letters "OEH" in the center.

"I've dreamed about it for months. After a lifetime of foot problems, it will be like my declaration that I am an overcomer in life..."

"Well, if nothing else, you're an uplift to the team...even if nobody pays attention to you." He pats my shoulder and walks off.

He's got that right. Finally, someone who admits my invisibility. If I were an uplifting person, you would think my positivity would spill over into my own life. I trek up the parking lot towards the school. The wind is bitterly cold, but I am so sweaty I don't want to throw on my hoodie. I check my phone to see if Mom is close, but she is not, and now I am even more discouraged than if I had not checked the tracking app. I guess this is a good time to sit on the curb like a homeless person and contemplate everything wrong in my life.

At the top of my list sits the sad fact I am the loneliest I have ever been, yet I am around more people than ever. I am overwhelmed with the amount of social interaction around me but lack of it directed *to* me. It is strange to be surrounded by hundreds of high schoolers only to be noticed by one or two...on a lucky day. I failed my Journalism test today...*journalism of all the classes!* That is supposed to be my easy A. I am surprised at how little I care about school, but then again, why should I care? I know I didn't study for it. Math has had my full attention. The last thing I need is to fail in math, and by doing so, seal my fate at track. Track is my life vest right now. Track, even if I run it as a lonely snail, teaches me endurance. But if I fail a test—boom!—off the team. Not even Coach Lakyn could guard me from this possibility. It is the school rule, and OEH does not play around.

Suppose the real reason I have not been pouring over homework is because I long for my Missouri relationships: with grandparents, friends, and even family time. I know, I know. My immediate family is physically *here*, but I rarely see them. With track practices extending and Journalism newscast deadlines, I am constantly in OEH Land. And admittedly, "home" doesn't exist. I simply return to a strange, gray house every night to my familiar bed in an unfamiliar room, falling asleep to the buzz of our neighbor's TV. There is no 'homey feeling.' I wish my grandma could come hug me and say everything is going to be okay, but what if it isn't? Who really knows?

What if we are stuck in this place forever? What if I never make friends at OEH and I am a permanent floater until the end of high school? I doubt I can even survive until then.

What if we are stuck in this place forever? What if I never make
friends at OEH and I am a permanent floater until the end of high
school? I doubt I can even survive until then.

"You have strep throat." The doctor's words send a chill through my body, reminding me I am still on this terrible planet called Earth. *Of course, I have strep. I probably caught strep from standing in the cold every day waiting on Mom after practice.* I think to myself, but I know better than to say this out loud. I am itching to run off this sticky doctor's table and into my own bed. It feels like unexpected sickness just shows up at the absolute worst times, like last summer when I found out I was moving. I really do think I am on a hidden camera TV show.

"Shshshmsmsmshsms…" I vaguely hear Mom and the doctor exchanging information about my prescription before I am tapped on the shoulder and hop off the table. I zip up my puffy, black winter coat and walk slowly to the car, thinking about all that just happened. *Ugh! I can't afford to miss anymore school days. I can't afford to miss a track practice—I'm already the worst runner on the team! I just can't be stuck in our rental house in my shared bedroom with nowhere to heal!*

"You'll have to text your coach and tell him you can't run at the first track meet," Mom pulls up directions on her phone—and that is one more annoying thing about moving to a new place: you hear Siri's irritating voice wherever you try to go.

Now that I am diagnosed with strep, this actually does disqualify me from track—even my upcoming school assignments. *And* I am nearly to my max on absent days.

I cry silently on the way home before tucking myself into bed and curling up into a ball. This doesn't even feel like home; it feels like a crowded motel room. It isn't even winter anymore when I can play Christmas jazz and sip chicken noodle soup. This is springtime; I am supposed to be tanning on the track, not blowing my nose under the covers.

As soon as Kelly leaves the room, I cry hard on my pillow until I am covered in slobber. And then I throw back the covers, wipe my face with some toilet paper, and run back to bed to do the same thing all over again. The lawnmower noise outside starts up just for my own frustration. A construction crew on the other side of the street is teasing me and blaring a Latino radio station. So, this is life.

"You've called in sick all week. Were you skipping school or something? 'Cause if so, I'll join you next time." Keli sits on the floor against the lockers and repaints her black nails.

"No," I throw my head against the wall. "I have been sick."

"You missed voting for student elections."

"Kinda don't care."

"Yeah, well, *your name* was on there."

"What, 'Cassidy'?"

"Your real name, dummy."

"Why was I on the list?" Someone must have thrown in my name in for a good laugh.

"You really think I would remember? Anyways, I don't think you have a shot. No need to worry. Carissa's name took over every category."

"You're encouraging." I roll my eyes. "Kidding."

I am not myself.

"You sure you want to run at the home track meet coming up?"

"What, do you keep a calendar of all the sports events?"

Keli stares at me uneasily like she can't tell if I am joking.

I am never this insensitive.

"Like Coach Stanley's mad-scientist loudspeaker voice doesn't stick in your mind. The whole school knows *'Mika McClain prepares to dominate OEH's home meet this Saturday!'"* She reenacts. "But you're not running, sick girl, are you?"

"Actually, I am." I reach for my math textbook. "Thankfully. Coach Stanley said it was my decision. And I don't want to a complete no-show like I dropped out because I wasn't good."

"You're not good?"

"I'm not. But I can't lose these track legs," I slap my used-to-be solid legs that are slowly dying away after I have been in bed the past week.

Keli laughs. "Even getting track legs wouldn't be worth running track for me."

I laugh and cough into my arm. Keli is a good friend in the most unusual way. You and I both know I am not the *best* athlete, if I am even an athlete at all, but track is the one thing I have going for me. It is my coping mechanism. And Keli believes in me.

But as Carissa and Callie appear far down the hall, I slowly back away from Keli and turn the other direction. I can't face them. I just don't have the energy.

"Where are you…"

"See you in class." I yell quickly.

When the bell rings at the end of the day and my eyes do their silent cry for a nap, I happen to stumble into Claire Dean. Perfect timing.

"You're back!"

What does she mean?

"Weren't you sick?" She asks when I don't respond. *C'mon, Candice. Think!*

"Oh, yeah. I had strep." I mutter. I used to get worked up and excited when a popular girl like Claire would talk to me. Now, I couldn't care less. My head is pounding like a gong, and I am so done with being at OEH. Please, someone ship me back to Missouri where I belong.

"You're going to track now, right?" She walks with me to my locker.

"Best part of the day," I calmly manage to say. It surprises me she knows my schedule. Still, why can't she just leave me alone?

"That's how I feel about cheer; you should really consider joining!" she says, turning to her locker decked out in sparkly cheer pictures. Oh, I see what she's getting at with the whole "be nice to Candice" façade.

"Sure. Thanks." My smile fades. And then, like I do every day at the bell, I grab my track clothes and head for the locker room. It's a wonder I don't just shut down Carissa's whole agenda to get me to join cheer and be part of their clique. Maybe I should just run up to the three of them one day and scream, *"Get lost!"* then run out of the double doors and catch an Uber to Missouri. It is obvious she is trying to keep me from becoming an individually popular figure in the school's eyes. Like I am a threat.

There is no time to think; I am entering the track world. I open the door to the locker room and walk straight to my corner away from everyone else. Rebecca, a long-distance runner and average junior with no personal hygiene awareness, is braiding her blond hair into Dutch braids and trailing dozens of stray oily hairs into the sink. Eliza and Stella, the freshmen girls, are already changed and are snapping mirror pictures. I am counting the seconds for Emma and Kinsley to walk in mid-conversation—as always.

"And then they told us our junior trip would have to be postponed to the first week of May."

"No way!"

"Way! I even called, like, all the other hotels and they're all booked!" Emma and Kinsley push open the doors. I used to try to look interested in their conversation, but they never once acknowledged it, so I stopped trying. I wait for Mika to come in. Maybe she will talk to me.

She hasn't come in. We only have two minutes to get to the track. I wait for everyone to leave so I can have the mirror to wash my face and breathe. Why is this so hard?

I slowly shove my school clothes into my track bag and sigh on my way out of the locker room...which is where I am going to be this time tomorrow...and the next day...and the next day. It is like a bad dream on repeat.

"Candice—" a hand grabs my arm while I am trying to quickly get past the remaining well-dressed students in the school building, since I am in short shorts and without makeup.

It is Mika. She is standing next to some grown-up looking guys, still in her school clothes. "Are you feeling better?"

No. I want to scream. I wish she could be my mentor or something. I need help. "It's all good, it was just a cold."

"Aw, I'm sorry," she sympathizes, and before she can say anything else, a boy pulls her by the arm.

"Let's go, Mik! We're going to be late!"

"Tell coach I won't be at practice today," she yells to me, running with her senior friends to the doors.

Bye, Mika.

I am sitting in Journalism class for what feels like an eternity. The clock hand is moving in slow motion, as if mocking my urgency to break out of this classroom. Mrs. Lajuana is telling the class about our end of the year final project, but I can't make out her words. I feel so numb and unreal, like I am living in another dimension. I mean, I am sane enough to get up and do what I am supposed to do—scan my student ID, grab my textbook, look interested in class, walk out—but it is getting really hard for me to actually live in the moment. I can stare at an object without talking or really thinking about anything.

Today I am overly sensitive yet aloof at the same time. I wish I knew how to make the pain go away so I could make it stop. I cry at the littlest things, and whenever I see myself get angry, I know it can be traced back to a deep hurt in my heart. But I am so weak I do not stay angry for long, like I am out of energy to fight back. Maybe it's because I have been neglecting my morning prayer time due to complete exhaustion from track. Or maybe I have just been too angry at God for moving me here that the last thing I want to do is talk to Him. Or both.

"…And that is what I expect from each of you. Comprehendè?" Mrs. Lajuana says, unpinning her thick, black hair from a bejeweled banana clip and letting it trail down her back. Everyone stares at her with blank expressions. Mrs. Lajuana looks directly at me, expecting my usual outstanding student attitude, but instead I avoid her gaze and drop my head in my lap. If this is all there is to life, Cassidy doesn't want anything to do with it.

Chapter Nine

CONSEQUENCES

"**C**AN I BORROW your phone?" Keli whispers to me in Bible class.

Mabrey overhears and shakes her head. "You can't go along using Candice just because she's nice," She defends. Leaning towards me she whispers, "She's already made two anonymous calls on my phone, you don't have to give it to her."

"I promise—I just need to call my step-dad," she pleads, sensing my reluctance. "Candice, *c'mon.*"

"No, you're going to call your gang friends and—"

"Shut up!" Keli lashes back.

"You can pretend to play nice and all, but..." Mabrey continues. Either she is downright mean, or she knows a lot about Keli's past that I don't.

"Who do you think I am? Some criminal?"

I decide to give Keli the benefit of the doubt.

"I'll give you my phone on break," I tell her. Mabrey gives me a warning look.

Who. Cares.

"Thanks." Keli hands me back my phone with only a bit of battery life leftover. Her face is red.

"Anything wrong?" I ask casually.

"It's nothing," she says quickly. And before I can ask again, she darts down the staircase.

⌐

"Mrs. Lajuana, please send Candice Gibbons to the office." Mrs. Gray's voice screeches on the overhead speaker.

Here it comes. I am getting in trouble for associating with Keli.

All week she has been 'sick' and absent. I have tried texting her, but in regular Keli fashion, she hasn't responded. Honestly, I don't even care that everyone's "oohing" at me as I stand from my desk and numbly walk to the principal's office. I would almost rather them drug test me or send me home for doing something bad than sit in class, as long as I could come back for track. At least I would have a break from OEH's bright lights, two-faced snobs, and checkered floors.

"Please sit down." Principal Vanderbilt is in a black funeral-type dress with her hair in a low, solemn bun. I glance at her computer, which has my student profile pulled up and my grades on display in the largest font imaginable. *Oh, great.*

"You're aware of your math grade, I presume."

"Yes ma'am. I was sick during the quarterly test, and so I tried to catch up when I got back. But it did not go the greatest. I did get a tutor!" My face pleads for mercy.

Her sympathetic eyes stare straight into me. "Are you...*okay?*"

I shift in my seat. My palms begin to sweat. I don't want to have to spill all of my emotions on my unsuspecting principal. "I've never had so much change in my life. It's so overwhelming."

"Do you have any friends?"

"No...um..." I hesitate. I am definitely not about to say Keli—that would surely get me drug tested. But if I say Callie or Carissa, she will suspect I am one of them, though I am not really sure what she thinks of them in general. I tell her the honest truth: no one in particular.

"Well, you are making a bigger impact on your grade than you know. God has brought you here for a reason." She encourages.

Sure, He did. To watch me sit by myself every day at lunch. To be scorned at by even the social misfits. To be an isolated PK with apparent confidence. To sacrifice every other afternoon at a sticky restaurant booth to learn basic math. To lose friends and family and familiarity in Missouri only to embrace the permanent feeling of vulnerability.

"But remember," Principal Vanderbilt's words wake me up from my sad thoughts. "You can't run at the track meet in two weeks if you don't get your math grade higher by at least half a letter grade."

What?! You mean I won't get to do the one thing I've looked forward to since starting OEH? All because I'm not academically inclined like the rest of these students? All of a sudden, I feel numb and hollow inside. If I can't run track because of my inability to do math, why am I here? My thoughts and emotions are turning dark. My lack of active concern over this scares me.

Another day flies by, and I didn't even bother to dress like Carissa or any of her cheerleader friends. I am back to my trusty black sweatshirt, jeans, and tennis shoes. I overheard Isabelle saying I had gone Gothic, but I could not care less. I am done with cliques. I am over the stereotypes. I am done with everything.

After track practice, I fling myself, along with my backpack and drawstring bag, onto my bed, where I just stare at the ceiling in utter exhaustion. I hear a soft knock on the door. Angel lets herself in and evaluates my current situation. "What?" I lash out, not bothering to look at her.

"You...you got a package." She stammers, dropping a hand-sized cardboard box on the floor before turning to leave.

"Wait," I call out. *What have I been doing these past two months? I've barely acknowledged my own siblings!* "Sorry. How was school?"

Angel brushes her brown bangs away from her eyes and shrugs her shoulders. "Third grade is hard. I miss being homeschooled. But Mom said she wanted me to try public school for this semester. It's so different. I never get to see…see you or Mom or Jordan or anyone." Her lip quivers like she is about to cry.

I slowly untangle my arms from my bags and rise off my trundle bed. "I feel ya," I say in a collected voice. "But we're going to get through this. There are only three more months and school's out, then we can spend the whole summer together. Besides, we will be in our new house by June, so everything's going to work out…" I hug her.

"But you're staying at OEH? Forever?" She pulls back from my arms. Her question catches me off guard. If I am really about to devote the next two years of my life at this school, when would I ever see my siblings? When would we ride our bikes together or go exploring on outdoor adventures? Now I am faced with what to do next year for school.

But first of all, I must decide if I am even going to live.

"Have you checked your phone?" Kelly runs into me coming out of the bathroom door.

"Ahh! Hey Kel. I never see you in between classes…?"

"I always come to this bathroom at 11:06." She says in a hurried voice, wiping tear stains from her eyes, and then stops to stare at me. *"Dad is in the hospital."*

"What?!"

"He…he started having heart palpitations and sweating and… and…" Kelly can barely breathe.

"Okay, okay. Calm down, Kel. Where is Mom?"

"With him at the hospital. Mrs. Jackson is going to pick us up after school. Oh, Candice. I'm so scared!"

"It's going to be okay." I say numbly.

DAD! Why dad? He's the most stable person in the world. With him in the hospital, I have the strongest feeling of vulnerability I have ever felt before in my entire life.

"Why didn't you call me?" I shout into the phone at Mom after school.

"Don't you think I tried? Kelly answered me after I attempted to call you!" She retorts.

I gulp back tears and pray aloud. *"Oh, God, help him."*

"I think we are going to be here all night. Are you okay to be alone?"

"Huh?"

"Candice, track with me."

"I am."

"We're going to be at the hospital all night. Are you okay with the kids at the rental house?"

"Sure." I say like I have a choice.

"Oh, and Candice…"

"Yeah?"

"Pray he is going to make it."

I run into his bedroom at the first light of dawn.

His body is lying motionless in the bed, wrapped in a white quilt tucked around his neck.

"Is he okay?" I whisper to Mom, who is barely awake herself.

"Don't touch him," she whispers sternly.

This is it. My dad died. Which means Candice dies, too.

This is not a time of sacrifice, a time of light, a time of influence.

Everything in my life has led to this sad, harsh reality.

This is *a time to die.*

My face pales as white as a ghost, fearing the worst. "Is he…?"

"He has shingles."

"SHINGLES?!"

"The doctor said he's going to be okay. Apparently, all his conditions are stress related." She says, closing her eyes and drifting back to sleep.

Oh, wonderful. Whew. Thank you, God. Thank you…thank you.

"But where's Keli?" I search the classroom for Keli's impactful presence. I have been asking around all morning seeing if anyone has seen her. I really need to talk to her.

"You haven't heard?" Callie looks uncomfortably around the room. "Keli's been expelled from OEH. She's not coming back."

"*What?*" My heart stops beating.

"Yeah, she got in trouble for something *really* bad. I think she is even getting kicked out of her foster home or something,"

"I heard it was something illegal!" Stevie Bowers enters the room.

But I don't care what Keli did. I cannot believe I will never get to see her again. Yesterday was my last day to sit beside her, and my last day to pour into her. A few weeks ago, she even asked me to explain a Bible passage she was reading in class. We started talking about God and the Bible and everything. She told me I was the nicest person she had ever met, and we really had a connection about what it means to authentically live as Christ.

I guess that was one thing I have done right all semester.

"Wait—didn't she use your phone to call someone the other day?" Callie sits up with a gossiper's adrenaline.

"Uh-huh," I slump further in my seat. *Oh, great.* What if people think I am tied to her illegal activities? What if I have to go to court and testify against her or something?

"Yeah, Cassidy. You and smelly Keli hang out together from time to time. Don't you?" Stevie remarks suspiciously.

"You better watch your phone, Candice." Callie jokes, but her words bounce off me.

I just can't believe Keli is gone. Who knows what kind of a life she has been living outside school walls?

I pass by the art classroom at the bell where student paintings adorn the walls. I stop at Keli's modern painting with letters and numbers of blue, red, and black. The title of her painting reads, "Kindergarten Scratches" and makes me laugh as a tear runs down my cheek. Keli had perfect dry humor and sometimes even the snobbiest of cheerleaders laughed at her jokes…or, maybe they were just laughing *at* her.

Why, Keli? Why would you do something to get you kicked out of a private school? And then I wonder if there was something I could have done to make her feel better. Maybe if I had not run off so fast when we stood by her locker talking, all because Carissa and her friends were coming. I could have invited her to youth group or offered to take her to out to coffee. I guess I just did not want to come across too "churchy." Moreover, I was so consumed with myself I never really noticed enough to care.

But now she's gone, and I will never have a chance to talk to her again.

I come home and run straight to my room, flinging myself on the bed. I can't take any more of this drama. It hits me that I am running out of time to make a mark on the world before I crumble into pieces. Dad's heart scare and Mom's stress is eating at me. I am not going to just stand by while people like Keli or Mabrey or even Claire enter and exit my life without any impact from me. I may feel like I am inwardly dying right now, but if it is the last thing I do, I *must* leave a mark on OEH. And it very well may be the last thing I do.

Chapter 10

THE SACRIFICE

W EDNESDAY NIGHT. 7:44 p.m. My eyes feel like they have been scorched by fire, and they look like it, because I accidentally slept in my contact lenses, which is like the equivalent of not closing your eyes all night. My hands are shaking from, I don't know, nerves, stress, and maybe as a side effect from my strep medication. My feet are tenderly sore and a shade purple from track, and because of my autoimmune disorder, my legs look like they've been beat up which happens when my heart rate is low and blood pools to my feet. Stress triggers that. To top it off, the youth pastor is speaking on depression. Go figure. It is not like I can even open up tonight and cry about my parents' problems or Keli's situation—not here—because this is not youth camp with Jaclyn. All I can do is tune out message and hope nothing sinks in. *Why am I even here?*

"...We can't do everything on our own. God has people around us who can lift us out of our mess. Depression comes in all forms. It is better to acknowledge it and seek freedom before it takes over your life. Sometimes the best thing you can do is ask for help." Says the youth pastor. The air conditioning kicks in, and I start to shake.

Tia is looking at me funny.

"You always shake." She pokes my goosebump-filled arm. "At 7:45 p.m. on the dot."

"Shhh," I tell her, because we are on the front row and it looks like she is talking to me about having depression or something, and now everyone is looking at us. *I don't have depression...do I?* I twiddle my ring. *I've never struggled with it before.*

"Sometimes depression can be hereditary, other times it can be triggered by traumatic loss..." the youth pastor keeps talking.

Anxiety stirs. *How do I get out of it?*

"If you need breakthrough, come down to the altar and let a leader pray over you,"

What will Tia think? And what about the Jacksons'? Who knows if Carissa is in the back of this auditorium?! God, will you help me please get help? I shiver, typing in a reminder on my phone to ask Mom about getting a counselor. But then I hesitate, wondering how she would respond. The last time I asked to see one, it didn't go so well.

"Are you kidding?" She had said, looking at me like I was from a different planet. "You don't need a counselor; you have me and your dad, plus all of your grandparents."

"It's just not the same," I choked back tears as an emotional pre-teen. It was the year I lost most of my friends and mentors. It was hard, but I made it.

But this time, I feel like I have a legitimate reason. I really do feel like giving up...and not just on OEH. Life is unbearably hard. I want to escape it. I don't know how I would do it or what I would do exactly. I haven't thought that far. I'm just sick and tired of being sick and tired; tired of the same routine, tired of seeing the same faces at school, tired of Mom's emotional problems and our family's instability, tired of our crowded rental house. Tired of it all!

"Candice, please stay after class." Mrs. Lajuana blurts out in front of the entire room. I barely heard her under my Journalism earbuds while I am editing this week's newscast.

"Ooooohhhhh," the class snickers.

Mika shuts it down. "Grow up."

I throw a tired smile of appreciation in her direction. She does not see it. I still can't believe I blew it with Keli. Why in the world did I value Carissa's approval over Keli's soul? Like, I am not even sure if she is actually a Christian. And there I was, living life like a selfish, clueless teenager, ignoring her when in the presence of the cheerleaders. How shallow is that?

The bell rings and the class scatters. I shut down my computer and take a deep breath, bracing myself for whatever Mrs. Lajuana is about to say. It's not as if life could get any worse.

"Candice, Candice, Candice..." she removes her glasses and leans back in her swivel chair. "What is *wrong* with you?"

"I'm really sorry I failed last week's journalism test—really!"

Mrs. Lajuana studies me with a puzzled expression. "Goodness gracious, girl. I couldn't care less about that. You're an A student as it is. But something is wrong, isn't it?"

"Everything." I admit.

"I see it on your face. In your blue eyes. *Mm-mm.* Is it your friend, Keli?"

"Partly," I fidget in my seat, wondering how much my little mouth is about to say. "And my dad had a really big health scare. I thought he was going to die."

"Oh, dear girl."

"But he didn't, don't worry. Actually, if you don't mind me sharing, I think I am depressed." I blurt out, suddenly wishing I hadn't.

Mrs. Lajuana simply nods like she already knows. "You've been through a lot of change this past semester."

"I know it's not like a huge change. People go through way worse stuff than this. I almost feel guilty for struggling if that makes sense."

"Change is change. Don't compare it." She shakes her head.

"I think I need a counselor," I add in a matter-of-fact voice.

"Yes," her hands tickle the keyboard. "I know of a few good counseling places in Oklahoma City. I'll email you a few options." She is reacting calmer than I anticipated.

"I...I don't know what to say." I stammer. "Thank you so much."

"Don't mention it." Mrs. Lajuana brushes off my words with her hand. "But you know what is really going to help you get through this season of change?"

"What?"

"Going home."

It takes a second for me to process her words. "You're right. But I don't have a home," I mumble, "ever since we left our cottage in Missouri."

"Not your *physical* home," she corrects. "But what do you mean you don't have a home?"

"Oh, I just mean I feel like my home is in Missouri. We're not homeless. Our family is staying in a rental house right now and we all feel like our lives are hanging in midair." I explain.

"Well, glad you're not homeless. But it's high time you go home to your heavenly Father. Get in touch with the core of Candice. Get real with yourself. Didn't you say you moved here to follow God's will?" She stands from her desk.

"Yes," I shrug, throwing my backpack over my shoulder and following her to the door. "At least I thought it was God's will. Now I'm not so sure."

"Sometimes God uses bad circumstances to see how strong our faith is in Him." Mrs. Lajuana points her finger to the sky. "Tests, hardships, they come after obedience. When you're close to God, it's as if you never go anywhere unfamiliar. And what follows after obeying God?"

"Sacrifices." I know this one.

"Eh, 'blessing' is the word I was looking for. Obedience comes first, then blessing. Like a child who obeys their parent. But who am I to say these things…you told me yourself God would bless you for moving here. Why walk away from the Gift Giver when you know He's holding your gift?"

I picture God in Heaven with a ginormous present, waiting for the right time to give me the gift. "I sure just wish He would hand it to me."

"Only He knows the perfect time. I am glad you asked for help. I will send you information for counseling. Until then, keep asking

God for faith to make it through one more day." Mrs. Lajuana pats my shoulder and gently pushes me out into the noisy hallway.

I will try to stand as long as I can, Mrs. Lajuana.

"Hi," I mutter awkwardly, sinking into the leather love seat. We are in the stereotypical counselor's office: dark, warm, and pen-drop silent. It is early evening, and the fiery late-spring sunset is dripping between closed blinds, highlighting floating particles of dust in the air. There is a heavy, intimidating desk in the center of the room with a cushioned chair stapled with leather behind it. Apart from these sensations, the design, the decor, and this counselor, are blurry.

"Tell me all about yourself." She watches me closely, flipping open a legal pad and popping the head of a ballpoint pen like I am being investigated.

I shrug at her comment. *Where do I even begin?* She has probably already judged me by my black OEH track shirt. I bet she thinks I am rich and stuck up. *And good luck figuring out who I really am,* I think. I used to be the confident, outgoing girl who knew she had a bright future. I was the one who included the new kids, was a leader at church, and played with my siblings. But now, I am just a drain to the human race.

I tell the counselor this. She scribbles down more words. Then, with a sympathetic look, she hands me a depression evaluation form and tells me to fill it out. I flip through the pages with a purposefully confused face. I act like I don't know what it is so she can tell me more about it. I want to be asked more questions. I am playing ignorant. I don't know why.

"You can skip the ones about your love life, drug use, and alcohol history," she guides, crossing out numbers 4, 7, and 21. I glance up as if to imply, *"How do you know what I've done?"* but she only smiles and pats me on the arm. "You're not a bad girl. Your mom told me you're just going through a lot upon moving here. Just answer what is applicable."

Sure, I will, cause most of the questions describe me at this present moment: *crying uncontrollably? Loss of appetite? Numb emotions?* Ask anyone. Now that I am looking at my symptoms on paper, I can hear the soundtrack to my life building up to the climax. Tears fill my eyes until I can no longer read what is on the pages. I circle 'yes' on nearly every question (except for 4, 7, and 21, of course). I could not be more thankful Mom agreed to send me to the counselor Mrs. Lajuana recommended. It is time the truth comes out.

I wipe tears from my cheeks and slowly walk out of the counselor's office, curling my knees to my chest in the car. Where is the faith I had when I was in bed from my wisdom teeth surgery? I wish I could be that resilient again. But it does give me hope that I *can* fight this; that I *will* make it through. In all honesty I do not feel any better after seeing the counselor, but that is because Mrs. Lajuana told me I needed to get right with God. I know I need to just sit down and do it.

I don't know when that will happen. With weekly counseling sessions squeezed in between track practice and math tutoring, there is no time to think. Coach Stanley keeps telling us to "get our eyes on the track" before the meet this Saturday, but my eyes are partly at a booth in Braum's trying to figure out math equations; partly crying in a counselor's office; and partly surveying teenagers in a hallway trying to figure out my social life.

"I have moderate depression," I tell Mom in the car. "There. You see? I am depressed."

"I can see that," is all Mom says back.

"Are you saying you knew all along?"

"I knew you were struggling," she rubs tired eyes. "I just don't have the emotional energy to handle all of your problems. I thought someone else could help you instead."

I stare at my reflection, bored of myself. "You helped me during spring break."

"You're welcome." She says flatly. "I've gotten worse since then."

It sounds like Mom needs counseling herself. "The counselor said it's called 'situational depression,' which means it should pass once I figure out my new life in Oklahoma." I explain. "But not just when I get it figured out socially. I know this, Mom, because just like when I had my mouth surgery last summer, I'll feel better when I get right with God. You know, fully accept His will. Fully obey Him and accept the sacrifices." I breathe a sigh of relief.

"You sound pleased," Mom takes her eyes off the road to study my face.

"I just know what I need to do!" Tears blot my eyes. "I knew I was losing myself, Mom. I thought I was going crazy or something. I just couldn't go on living that way. I thought I didn't have a choice but to cave in. I almost didn't make it."

Mom remains silent. I can't tell if she's angry at me or just shocked to hear her oldest daughter announce past suicidal thoughts. I am waiting on her to tell me it's all going to be okay and that we can get ice cream and chat, and everything will work out—but Mom is different. I have never seen her like this before. "We *all* feel that way." she says darkly.

All I can control is myself. I have shut myself in the pantry. It is the only place I can get away and think. I am writing in my journal, tears staining the pages. *Well, I called it like it is. Are you proud of me?* I whisper aloud to God. I hope He is listening. *Anyways, it's me; Candice. The same girl you spoke to about doing something 'big' last summer. So, here I am, in Oklahoma, trying to fulfill my calling at this random school where no one like me. Any thoughts?* I reach for my brown leather Bible and flip to Romans where spot a verse I underlined years ago at summer camp. It is four lines long and written in tiny, black Times New Roman: "We can rejoice, too, when we run into problems and trials, for we know that they help us develop endurance. And endurance develops strength of character, and character strengthens our confident hope of salvation."

And since I am a literal person, I believe and accept this. I flip back to the Old Testament and land on Psalm 119, a chapter I used to read every morning. One of the verses I circled during my wisdom teeth surgery pops out at me: "My suffering was good for me, for it taught me to pay attention to your decrees." God is answering with specific words: "Rejoice in our confident hope. Be patient in trouble and keep on praying." Says another line in Romans. "Whether we like it or not, we will obey the Lord our God to whom we are sending you with our plea. For if we obey him, everything will turn out well for us." Wrote the prophet Jeremiah. "Though the Lord gave you adversity for food and suffering to drink, he will still be with you to teach you." I read in Isaiah.

I write all these verses in my journal and smile amidst tears. *He answered! He actually answered!* This is the best I have felt since last fall when I trusted God with my life. Since then, doubt from outside circumstances has crept into my thoughts. But I can get back on track. I am reminded of the verse in Isaiah Dad said related to one of the prophecies about our family:

> "For I am about to do something new. See, I have already begun! Do you not see it? I will make a pathway through the wilderness, I will create rivers in the dry wasteland."

To imagine my world full of color, excitement, and meaningful purpose sounds unattainable. But didn't God say my life would be full of joy if I followed Him? I read in Matthew:

> "You are the light of the world—like a city on a hilltop that cannot be hidden. No one lights a lamp and then puts it under a basket. Instead a lamp is placed on a stand, where it gives light to everyone in the house. In the same way, let your good deeds shine out for all to see, so that everyone will praise your heavenly Father."

Okay, God. I'm ready to be a light to my school. But only if You will help me. Just please give me one more chance.

"Hey Candice, come sit by us." Claire motions to me across the chapel auditorium.

Thank you, God. One less Friday to face a seating predicament.

Last week I had to sit with three confused freshmen. Talk about being desperate. But this week I am thankful for another interaction with the cheerleaders. I realized I had been putting them in a stereotype as much as I had with the drug kids. After all, they are real girls just like me. And I am not going to waste another opportunity to influence someone at OEH. I promise.

"Students, today we will be hearing from a missionary who is currently serving in Kenya." Principal Vanderbilt passes the mic to a short, scrawny millennial who's overdue for a facial shave. His clothes are wrinkled and raggedy, and he fits the perfect picture in my mind of a sold-out-to-God missionary—someone I wanted to be as a kid. Even now, I still kind of consider myself a missionary. At least, I *want* to be one.

I squeeze in a seat between Callie and Claire. My curls have fallen out, my black jeans are three sizes too small, and I am already starting to sweat in this hot room.

Mr. Kenya has not even begun his life story.

"I bet most of you have lived pretty comfortable lives," he finally says.

These jeans are killing me.

"I have the privilege of serving in Kenya through a ministry that shares the love of Jesus with kids who have lived unimaginable lives…" he goes on to share various testimonies about God raising up leaders from impoverished situations. I feel like my legs are suffocating and I cannot focus, so I resort to picking at a loose thread on my sleeve.

"And that's why we need leaders like you in America. So, okay. I feel like God's calling me to ask you to do something uncomfortable…" His words wake me up. "On the count of three, everyone who feels like God is calling them to be a light to their school…I want you to stand."

I nearly choke. *Could he be more descriptive without shouting my name?* This is a chance to redeem myself, a chance to rise up and be the leader I am called to be. But there is no way I would rise in front of the entire school and pronounce myself a leader. *No way.* I plan to do this the hidden way. I will lead subtly, thank you very much Mr. Kenya.

"Don't be embarrassed; if you are called to be a leader, this is your time to stand."

You've got to be kidding me.

"And out of respect for these students' decisions, everyone close your eyes. This is a personal moment between them and God…" he adds.

My heart is pounding like a machine gun.

God, you already know I'm a leader, so we're good. Right? I pray. But then I realize, I in order for me to really influence OEH, I guess I need to prove it to myself.

"…Last time I'm asking." The missionary warns, and this whole moment strikes me of the similarities of a church altar call, where people make their decisions to follow Christ—the scariest and most defining moment of your life. Like this one for me. My palms are sweaty. My legs feel paralyzed. My heart has stopped beating. I know what I have to do.

"Stand up!" He commands. I wrongly peak around the room and only spot two or three overconfident seniors out of their seats. *At least I wouldn't be the only one standing…* I sigh in a trembling voice. It sounds like a gasp of air.

Without allowing procrastination to dominate, I force my sandbag legs to a standing position. My eyes are squeezed tightly as if to ensure the closure of anyone else's that may be open. But I did it.

"God bless you," the missionary breathes in the microphone. It's as if he directed it specifically towards the frizzy-headed sopho-more in the row of cheerleaders. While he prays over us, I pray sin-cerely as I can pray. And as he closes with an "amen," my legs retreat like a magnet to the seat in such a speed that neither Claire nor Callie should have suspected anything.

I am awake now.

Perhaps God never spoke audibly, but this is a defining moment. A moment I proved myself ready to accept my calling as a leader— with or without friends. Who cares if I make the "in-crowd" or win the track girls' approval? Keli taught me that it can be as simple as caring for one person. So, for the rest of my time at OEH, I am determined to stand for Christ.

"I want each of you to pick your word of the year. It can be anything from 'health' to 'progress' to even an emotion you feel towards life, such as 'blessed.' You are required to illustrate the word on the back." Mrs. Abernathy flops a paper on each of our desks in English class. "At the end of the hour, everyone is going to go around and share why they chose their word."

I rest my chin in my hand and immediately begin drawing. I know what my word is going to be. I trace a cross in the center and a border of thorns around the edges of the paper. I write the word *SACRIFICE* in big letters across the page and add little stick people at the foot of the cross. Though I have never been much of an artist, I am pleased with the final product of my illustration, and I am excited to share with my class what I overcame this semester. Maybe when I show my illustration it will speak to people's hearts.

"Sorry, Candice. It looks like we're out of time. You can stay after class and share your word with me." Mrs. Abernathy tells me at the bell.

Nevermind. I am tempted to crumble my paper into a ball and walk to my next class, but then I figure I would be mad about wasting so much time over the drawing only to throw it away, so I inch over to her desk and set the paper in front of her.

"Why 'sacrifice'?"

"Because our family chose to leave Missouri to move here. And though no one promised it would be easy, moving has been much harder than any of us anticipated. My dad was so stressed he had heart palpitations and was in the hospital. Mom is falling into depression and is isolating herself from the family. And I'm sure my siblings are each facing their own issues, but the one I know best is my own. I lost trust in God. I was so certain He would use me to influence the students at OEH in a particular way—an organized way—but instead He chose a messy route. I lost all of my influence because I fell into depression. And when Keli left, I felt like I lost the one person I had the opportunity to reach. Sacrifices really do come after obeying God's will." I gasp for breath and stare at my feet. "Even though I gave up on God, He didn't give up on me. Because I don't know if you've seen this, but there's a pattern in the Bible: obedience comes first, then sacrifice, and then blessing. Well, I obeyed God last year by moving, so this year must be the sacrifice. And then, even if it doesn't happen for a while, I know God is going to bless me for moving here."

Mrs. Abernathy is speechless. I don't know whether it was right to spill out my entire story to my English teacher, but then again, maybe it was not me speaking.

"I have no doubt you will be blessed, Candice." She smiles. "And I *know* you are going to make an impact on the students at OEH."

"I hope so," I say, shifting my backpack and checking my watch. I have thirty seconds to run to Oklahoma History class. "Well, thanks for listening." I add awkwardly, turning to leave.

"Oh, wait just a minute." She rises from her desk. "A while ago, you were sick, and on one of those days the class wrote notes for each other in these paper bags." She removes one of the bags from the wall with my name on it. "Let me see here…"

It looks empty to me. She should not have bothered with mine.

"I'm afraid it's not much, but I still wanted to give yours to you." She smiles sympathetically. "You better go to class!"

"Thanks." I say, discreetly squeezing the bag to see if I can feel anything.

I think there is one note. But who would give it to me?

All day I have been curious. Was it Mrs. Abernathy out of sympathy? Or maybe a joke from Stevie the rhino boy? As soon as I arrive home, I unzip my backpack and search for the sack. That is when I notice the mysterious package Angel brought in that has been in the corner of my room for weeks. I haven't even bothered to see who it is from. Setting my backpack aside, I reach for the package and study the Missouri address. Inside the package is a note and a bag of hair scrunchies.

> *Candice,*
>   *We miss you being at the farm every weekend. Your mom said that moving has been the hardest on you in particular and I wanted you to know that we've been praying for you. Change is really hand and I totally understand that. I hope life in Oklahoma continues to get better and you find some good friends. Hopefully, we can come watch one of your track meets soon. Enjoy this little happy package.*
>   *Love, Aunt Angela*

My eyes fill with tears, and I reread the note. Aunt Angela has no idea how needed and timely this note speaks to my circumstances. And oh, how I have missed being at my grandparents' farm with the cousins and aunts and uncles! Her words make me smile and cry all at the same time. The ache of missing Missouri burns. I wipe away my tears and picture Aunt Angela's face. She would tell me to stay strong and keep doing what I am supposed to do. And even if all of my Missouri friends and family miss me, they know I moved here because of God's will. It is not like I can go back on my promise to trust God with my life.

I suck in the tears and return to searching for the Mrs. Abernathy handed me. When I find it in the bottom of my crummy front pocket, I tear it open and hold up the note to the light.

"But those who trust in the Lord will find new strength. They will soar high on wings like eagles. They will run and not grow weary. They will walk and not faint."—Isaiah 40:31

—*Coach Lakyn*

It was Coach Lakyn herself! How in the world did she get to do this? I hold the note to my heart and thank God for people like Aunt Angela, Mrs. Lajuana, and Coach Lakyn. Does this verse not describe the very problems I have wrestled with? Running and not growing weary?

Now I am assured: I am in the right place at the right time.

Ever since I asked God for another chance to be a light at OEH, I feel the peace and joy I used to have. It is like no matter what happens, I know I am going to be okay. I think counseling is actually working. Every morning I have been thanking God for my life; even the parts that I don't understand—like why I have to sit in tutoring to understand math laws that He created—can't He just teach me? But it is teaching me endurance.

Of course, I am still not Miss Influencer at school. But I am processing my emotions with my counselor, and she is teaching me how depression is not a stigma, but a true emotional imbalance. She said this season is going to pass, just like other hard seasons in the past. And I am learning to sympathize with slow learners like me out there who need help with school or changes like moving. I understand how other kids feel when they have to drop everything and begin a new life. What about my social status at OEH? Well, if all I do is overcome my physical obstacles by running just one race at track, if all I do is show kindness to kids who will never return the favor, or even do something as simple as making efficient videos for

Journalism—if that's what God wanted me to do all along—I will be satisfied.

Thank you, God, and my dear tutor, Amy Kim, and that sticky booth at Braum's! I skip out of the office into the echoey atrium, silent at the moment. As I walk back to class, I stretch out my arm and pray for each classroom door, feeling like my old self. God, I pray for all the cheerleaders in chemistry right now. I pray that you would use me to be a light to the awkward girls in the robotics class. I may still be sorting through my emotions, but I am not going to let my feelings get in the way of impacting students' lives. Bring on the challenges!

Chapter Eleven

RUN, CANDICE!

A SATURDAY-MORNING STILLNESS HAS settled over the house until my 5:30 a.m. alarm that sounds like a flock of birds. I turn it off and roll over, aggravated that I did not turn it off last night.

But then I shoot up in bed. *Today is the big track meet.*

I have dreamed about this day for months; the opportunity to wear my track jersey, tighten my hair, and screw in my running spikes just like a true athlete. This is my time!

I leap from my bed as if the 400-meter race is about to start and cook a grand breakfast of frittatas, whole-grain toast, a green banana, and a blueberry smoothie. Then I load bags of grapes, salty pretzels, and electrolyte waters for snacks in between races. If it had not been for Emma, I wouldn't have known what to pack snack-wise. I feel quite accomplished staring at my lunch bags and hot breakfast plate.

Every little thing matters. I carefully chew each bite.

"Every second makes a difference!" I remember Coach Stanley yelling during the last stretch of our practice race.

I stare at my stone-cold face and pull my hair into a high, intimidating ponytail. "You show them what Candice is made of," I whisper aloud. Flashbacks of dance performances which led to foot surgeries play in my mind, and I envision all of the strength training

I have done during the past three months and all of the grueling ladder drills. But this is different than any dance performance. I do not know what is going to happen. I try to remind myself that it's as simple as a *100-meter* and *400-meter*. But can I even *run* the 400-meter? We will see.

Coach Stanley prepared me the best he could these past two months to run with endurance. But you can only train a tortoise so much. The fact that I finish last at every practice should be a clear indicator of what is going to happen today. They say, "how you train in the dark determines your time in the light," which probably means practice makes perfect, or something like that. Regardless, there is no hope for little Candice aside from divine intervention. I think the 100-meter is going to be easy if all I think about is getting from one stretch to the other as fast as I can. I will pretend a clown is chasing me. And maybe, by the end of this semester, I will be able to run the 400-meter completely at lightning speed. But you've got to start somewhere. For today, I am just praying I can survive.

I slide on my red track jersey. Representing OEH by wearing the school logo is daunting. I hate to let our team down and finish embarrassingly late. I can just imagine Emma, Kinsley, and Stella standing next to Coach Stanley at the end of the track with horrified looks on their faces, not daring to look, as a cloud of dust forms… *"Oh look, there's another runner limping down the track!"* followed by cheers in the stands, *"You can do it! Finish strong!"* like I am some dumb kid who forgot I was racing. This is an extreme, but not completely farfetched.

I throw on my OEH hoodie and stare down at my feet. My pinky toes already feel swollen, and my big toes are turning in like a curve in the road. Hopefully nobody notices my odd feet when I put on my spikes at the starting line. I grab my neon drawstring bag packed carrying spikes, extra socks, and a water bottle for the finish line. I stuff this bag along with my lunch in my black backpack and text Mom to make sure she's awake. It is 6:49 a.m., and we have to be there by 7:00 a.m. I recall the conversation from Thursday when Stella nearly threw a fit as Coach Stanley announced the show-up time…

"But it's a *Saturday*, Stanley!" She whined, rolling her eyes in disgust. "We never show up to track meets that early!"

"Yeah, and it's also our first track meet of the season which happens to be on our turf. I need both the girls' and boys' teams to help set up all of the events."

Stella moaned in anguish.

"Can we take a nap once we set up the tents?" Asked Emma hopefully.

"Why would I care?" Coach laughed in his strange manner. "No, actually, you'll need to be down on the track warming up in the event before yours, so look at the schedule…" he handed out an order of the track meet. I thoroughly studied it and noted the 100m was one of the first events listed. "But I don't care what you do outside of that." He finished. "You're single."

"Sweet," said Emma, casting a side glance to Kinsley.

"And are we allowed to wear our sweatshirt over our uniform up until our event? 'Cause if the weather's anything like today, there are gonna be icicles on my forehead." Stella added.

"There'll be a tent up on the hill against the back of the school that all the OEH track kids will be at. Keep your stuff there." Coach Stanley then turned to me, "Coach Lakyn said she talked to you about running the 400-meter dash. You still on?"

And it must have been amusing for the team to watch me—a new duckling—say yes. Even though I would have jumped at the chance to back out of the 400-meter, perhaps out of pride, or maybe even a hint of determination, I didn't. But today, it seems like the biggest regret of my life. *Why couldn't I just be content to run the quick and easy 100-meter race?* "I feel like I am about to throw up." I tell Mom in the car. Mom and I are both morning people, so we get along best on the drive to school. But anything after 9:00 p.m., we are both dangerous. The black stillness of the morning is strangely energizing—I feel like I am being filmed for one of those motivational videos showing an athlete getting up before dawn.

"Can you believe what you're about to go…*achem*…do?" Mom coughs. She sounds sick, but I don't really notice. A dozen butterflies migrate into my stomach.

"Oh, I can believe it, 'cause I feel the nerves." I laugh.

"But look how far you've come; just two years ago you were in a wheelchair," Mom remembers. Oh, I remember, alright. It was the longest two months I have ever had: trapped in double casts up to my knees. "Hey, guess what! Gigi and Poppy are going to drive in from Missouri to watch you run!"

"No way! Really?"

"Yep! Look for them in the bleachers. But seriously, Canzie, are you sure your feet are ready for this?"

"Don't ask, I might just not show up." I warn. I have not given myself time to think about my feet. I think about everything that has led up to this moment: running for years by myself, training early mornings and late afternoons, seeking out Coach Stanley, and boldly committing to track. This is not just a physical obstacle, but a mental challenge.

"Actually, I was born for this moment." I say as we turn in the school parking lot. "Everything God has allowed into my life has prepared me for this exact day. This is a monumental accomplishment in the life of Candice Gibbons."

"That's right! You get out there and show them what Candice Gibbons is made of!"

"Yeah; pins and screws and tortoise superpowers!"

Before I can blink, I am standing next to the starting line for the 100-meter dash.

"Let's go, let's go!" Coach Stanley taps Kinsley and I on the shoulder to take off our sweats. "It's time, girls."

"You ready?" Kinsley asks me, bending down to tie her spikes.

"I guess we have to be," I quickly answer, caught off guard. *C'mon, Candice! Why couldn't you say something like, "Yeah! Are you?"* My inner critic coaches. But I have no time to make up for it. Right now, I am a sprinter.

"Girls 100-meter dash runners, go to your lanes," I hear, and I replay in my mind the way to use starting blocks. I am thankful this meet is on our track—a familiar track—and not somewhere new. Kinsley is in Lane 3 to my right, which makes this feel like another practice if I do not look in the stands.

"*Go Candice!*" I hear a voice yell. A feeling of confidence and fear sweep through me as I see Gigi and Poppy wave from the bleachers. *They drove all the way here to see me run!* I see Dad and Kelly with them, too. *But where is Mom?* I wonder, shaking my legs and arms like everyone else is doing.

"Runners take your marks," a voice on a megaphone booms in front of my lane. I realize I am now the only still shaking my legs and everyone else is down in position. *Touch toes. Position hands. Crouch down. Left foot up, right foot bent.* I repeat in my mind. *God, please help me to run fast. And please, if possible, help me not to be last.* I pray, immediately realizing how dumb that must sound; most girls are praying to win.

Three voices interrupt my intense pre-race prayer from Lane 1. I notice a girl without a track uniform being helped into position. She doesn't even have running blocks. "Excuse me, can we have a minute?" Her coach says to the guy holding the megaphone. They begin explaining to the girl how to get in position. She looks scared to death—this is probably her first race ever. Oddly enough, this makes me feel better about the race. I decide it is my personal mission to beat her (even if I do have the advantage of knowledge). I notice two girls beside Kinsley stand up and start stretching again.

"Why aren't they down in blocks?" I whisper to Kinsley.

"It's intimidation; there's always a girl or two who wait last minute so that everyone will think they're super good."

"Oh." I stare at the two tall, muscular, and fierce-looking girls from St. Luke's Prep School who make eye contact with each of us on the ground.

"Ladies, *please.*" The guy says to them away from the megaphone. The suspense to begin this race is killing me—especially because now there is a girl I have a chance to beat.

"Runners take your marks," the man repeats.

The crowd falls silent.

"Get set…" I close my eyes and listen.

The squeaking of my spikes pushing up makes my heart thump faster. I glance over at the rest of the girls' blocks, who remind me of synchronized swimmers in slow motion. Ironically, I don't feel as many butterflies as before. I feel competitive—like I am here to fight against my weaknesses. *Feet, you don't have control over me. I am speed.*

"*Go!*"

Everything is happening like a lightning bolt. I breathe in and out so fast I can't run a step in between. Blurry figures race past me in colored jerseys and I feel a glimpse of hopelessness when I realize I am still halfway to the finish line. Then I realize one person is behind me—catching up by the second—and I know I can beat her. I push up on the balls of my feet and slice my arms in the wind.

"*Run Candice!*" I barely see Gigi stand up off the bleacher.

"*Come on girls! Cheek to cheek!*" Coach Stanley yells from the sidelines. My heart is racing so fast I have no time to think about my running posture. As we near the finish line, Kinsley zooms past me. The new girl is at my heel. But I am *not* going to let her beat me in my first race. I grit my teeth and duck my head as the white line approaches. She does too.

"*Run Samantha!*" I hear her coach scream ahead of us. Samantha may be fast, but she's dealing with little Candice—who has enough determination to move from a new state and join a new sport and expect to "win" first round.

We are the only runners still on the track. Three seconds and I will have won the race.

One ahead. Two ahead. Three ahead…

Applause fills the stands as I collapse onto the track. I know they're not clapping for me—second to last loser—but I pretend they are.

I didn't come in last!

Samantha looks disheveled. Part of me wants to do the whole "good job" thing and pat her on the back, but my legs are on fire—like sizzling volcano lava—and my heart won't stop panicking. *Pull yourself together.* I tell myself, but everything is starting to spin. I see

Kinsley receive the first-place medal, and the boys 100-meter dashers step onto the track.

"Candice!" Dad yells from the fence holding my spike bag. Thank goodness I put a water bottle in there. I push myself off the track and limp towards him like a fighter from the ring: puffing out my chest, tilting my chin, and flashing a smile to show I am happy. I *am* happy, after all. If I did not feel like I am near-death right now, I might actually be able to carry on a conversation.

But I am exhausted. I might need hospitalization. *C'mon, it was a 20-second ordeal. Don't make it worse than it is.* I think to myself. My body disagrees. "Need—water—now—" I gasp. Having POTS, my autoimmune disorder, I am prone to be lightheadedness and nausea after any physical activity. I am used to it, but it does not make it any easier.

"Here's your water." Dad helps me off the track. He has his phone propped in his left hand, which means he is videoing me.

"Hi," I say awkwardly to the camera.

"So, tell us," He hands me my bag. "What was it like running your first race?"

At this moment, I want to tell the camera that track was a complete mistake. Why in the world would I join a sport that would physically kill me—and lose dignity in the process? It seems like a no-brainer. Track is simply *not* for me. But then I cast a side glance to the inner soccer field and see Samantha lying on the grass. I remember how I beat her—I actually beat her—in my *first* race. "It was… amazing."

"Great job at the track meet on Saturday!" Mika says to me in Journalism the following Monday. We do not usually interact in class; I think it is because she is around her group of senior friends then. But today, she seems extra friendly.

"Thanks!" I glance up from my computer screen. "Track's definitely not a walk in the park."

"Tell me about it." She rolls her eyes.

As if. It's not like Mika just won a medal at the track meet on Saturday for the fasted 800-meter race. "You were fabulous," I smile, still in shock that such a talented girl could be so hard on herself. "Are you going to run in college next year?"

"Yeah." She stands up from her desk and stretches her sore legs. "I've got three scholarship offers. It's a lot to juggle..."

"Something I wouldn't mind juggling," yells a baseball kid from across the room. Several students laugh.

"Give us a break, Mika." The baseball kid continues. "You were a school record setter, Miss Outstanding OEH, and have been the lead news anchor for Journalism for galaxies. What else do you have to prove?"

Mika sits down.

"Just because she tries hard doesn't mean she's a snob," I interject. Everyone stares at me, shocked to hear me speak. There I go again...

"Ooooohhhhh," the class snickers. The baseball kid throws up his hands and turns back to his work. I see Mrs. Lajuana in the corner of my eye smiling at me.

"Thanks for what you said," Mika says when the class clears at the bell.

"Don't mention it," I throw my backpack over my shoulder and start to walk out. "I've...been praying for you lately." I add awkwardly, stopping at the doorway.

"Um, thanks. I really appreciate that." Mika says, hesitant to be vulnerable. After all, she is Mika McClain, the school legend. "You're a really cool sophomore."

"Thanks," I straighten my posture and tilt my chin the way Carissa does when someone compliments her. And then Mika and I begin to walk out together, and I feel so cool and popular. Upbeat 2000's background music is playing in my head, and that feeling of being in a movie is creeping up on me.

"Just a minute, girls." Mrs. Lajuana's voice halts our happy exit from class. Mika and I quickly turn around. "You are aware that your end of the year music video project is due in two weeks, correct?"

"Got it." Mika gives a thumbs up and turns on her heel, immediately greeted by adoring fans in the school hallway. I, on the other hand, inch towards Mrs. Lajuana's desk.

Oh no. I totally forgot about this project. What am I going to say?

"M-music video?"

"Yes, the same one I have been talking about for the past month." Mrs. Lajuana gives me a teacherly glare. "You are working on it, aren't you?"

I set a reminder on my phone. "I...er...well, I am now."

Thankfully, Mrs. Lajuana does not act too concerned. "I expect nothing less than a top-quality music video. Five minutes max. Be sure to include music copyright credits at the end."

"Got it," I start to walk away.

"Oh, and Candice," she calls out.

"Yes ma'am?"

"I have high expectations for your video in particular."

Chapter Twelve

THE PARTY

"**W**ELL?" CARISSA WHISPERS behind me as I slam my locker door. She has not said one word to me for weeks. I assume she is talking to someone else. *"Earth to Candice..."* she waves her hand stacked with rings. Her beach blond hair is wavy and halfway up with a pink velvet scrunchie.

"Oh, hi." I greet nonchalantly. Callie is watching us from a distance, and I am trying to remember to keep my cool. I feel like God would want me to be nice to them no matter what rumors have spread about me standing up in chapel. I am sure there were plenty.

"So, are you going to the party or not?" Carissa looks at me peculiarly. "You did get invited; you know."

"What party?" I ask calmly. I hope I don't sound surprised.

Carissa sighs impatiently. "Callie's having her sixteenth birthday party tonight and you're on the invite list. You should have gotten a text about it...unless there is another girl that has a Missouri area code in our school."

The truth is, I have not checked my phone all day. I have been looking for opportunities to interact with students. But now I quickly pull it out of my backpack and see a notification list that's a mile long, all belonging to *"Callie's 16th Birthday"* group chat.

"Oh, that is so cool!" I exclaim to Carissa.

"Yeah, well, I just thought it was cool you were invited in the first place. We haven't seen you around much…" she hints, examining her manicured nails.

"I have been eating my lunch in Journalism class to work on my final video project." I say, which is true.

"Hey, ladies." Callie joins our circle, flashing a perfect Colgate smile. "So, is she going?" she turns to Carissa. And then their eyes turn to me.

Images flash in my mind of the Galantine's dinner, of locker room days, of being left out of hall conversations and lunch rides. I feel sick to my stomach. The last thing I want to do is face popular girl problems again. But did not I ask God for a chance to impact *all* kinds of OEH students? Maybe this means going to the party. "I'll be there."

Both blonds exchange surprised glances.

"Wow, seriously?" Callie says in a sincere voice. "We thought…I mean, you have kind of drawn away from the world this past month. You're not mad at us or anything, right?" Now Carissa shares the same genuinely concerned expression, and for the first time God allows me to see these girls as average sophomores just trying to find their way in life.

"Right, I'm sorry. I have been dealing with a bunch of emotions ever since moving here. But I'm all good now." I flash a smile.

"Great. Well, we've missed you. You know, the offer still stands about joining cheer. We'd…love it if you would reconsider." Carissa fiddles with her gold hoop earring and looks me over to make sure I had not gained weight or anything.

"I'll think about it," I promise. And then both girls walk off, leaving me to my own bewilderment. Did I *really* want to go to Callie Winters's 16th birthday party? I am shocked my name even appeared in the group chat. But like I said, this could be my ticket to making a difference at OEH. Still, this does not help me with the decision of whether I should come back here for school next year. Why can't God give me a clear sign?

"Hey," says another valley girl voice to my left. But this voice is softer, and audibly recognized as less of a threat. I turn around and see Claire Dean packing her Kate Spade backpack with glittery black notebooks.

"Hey," I smile. In the past, I would have felt so inferior I would have tripped over my words. But I am not intimidated. "Are you going to Callie's party tonight?" I ask, though I already know she is.

"Yeah, I'm going." She shrugs, rolling her eyes.

As we slowly walk past the rows of red lockers, I attempt to keep the conversation going. "What are you wearing to the party?"

"I have no idea!" She confides, her dazzling smile radiating across her face.

"Me neither!" I relate, though I seriously doubt Claire is actually concerned over her apparel. It seems like every day she has a new designer look.

"I heard some girls saying they were going to wear jumpers." She whispers like it's top secret. "And knowing Callie, she'll want us all in spring pastels for pictures."

"Alright. I guess I'll just wear something...springy."

"Cool. See ya," Claire waves, spotting her boyfriend, Nate, across the room.

"See ya," I wave back. Our paths separate as I walk to my next class with a gigantic knot in my stomach. *I can't believe I am going to a party tonight!*

It is 5:30 p.m. and my hair is soaking wet. Not only is my face completely bare, but I've even racked mom's closet looking for a springy outfit with no luck whatsoever. "Mooooom! I need fashion help ASAP!"

I hear Mom's footsteps down the hall. "What you have on looks great." She half-glances over my outfit.

"You really think so?" I feel a tad bit skimpy and casual in these tight jean shorts, white tank, and pink cardigan. It looks *decent*, like a good summer day arrangement, but *not* a multi-millionaire girl's birthday extravaganza. I feel more like a teen extra in one of those shows where they use laughing sound effects.

"Well, what else were you thinking?" She asks, and I turn my head to the heap of clothes scattered on the bed. "Oh."

"The party starts at 6:00 p.m. and her house is twenty minutes away. I've got to go dry my hair. I guess this will have to do." I conclude, shoving the unwanted clothes in my closet.

"I'll be ready to pull out at 5:45 p.m." Mom echoes down the hallway.

I scrambled to dry my hair and throw on some makeup, but time is working against me. It is now 5:47 p.m. and we're just now pulling out, but I forgot my sunglasses, so we are turning around. If it was anything else, I would have just left it, but Mom agrees these are essential to my spring outfit. Once I hop back in the car with my $10.00 gas station shades, I feel just a little more confident about my overall appearance. My hair dried in supernatural time and my makeup is on with no major glitches. And maybe it is just me, but I feel like the passenger window has some sort of magical filter that puts an innocent glaze on your face. I smile at my reflection and feel a few less butterflies in my stomach. "*Maybe I will fit in after all...*" I mutter and Mom hears it.

"You look fabulous! Besides, what can happen in just a few hours?"

Anything can happen in four hours. I don't say this aloud because I need Mom on my side. If anything happens, I need her to be ready to come snatch me out of the clique society. Not knowing what else to do with myself on this never-ending drive to the Country Club, I scan through the list of contacts in the group chat. *Whew, an all-girls party.* I smile to myself. And then I laugh at the list of the girls invited: *Claire, Carissa, Carey...*you name it. They all sounded so...*preppy.* I imagined all their fake smiling faces squished together in slow motion. They definitely fit the stereotype for cheerleaders. But I have got to remember to see them as girls just like me. After all, we were raised in entirely different worlds. I cannot blame them for acting rich and stuck up when that is the world they grew up in.

As we pull in the Country Club, Mom and I are in shock. Not only is this my first time *in* a Country Club, but this one even sur-

passes the ones I have seen in the movies. The houses look like cha-
teaus, each with what appears to be private lakes in their backyards.
A security guard stops us at the entrance. Big Roy has never rattled
so loudly.

"Yes?" He notes our not-so-luxurious car and Mom in her
workout clothes.

"Hi, we are here for Carissa, ugh…"

"Callie Winters's 16th birthday party." I pipe in. The man stares
at us suspiciously before a Porsche rolls up behind us and he waves
us on out of convenience. As Mom pulls onto the driveway, I can't
help but notice the row of 16-year-old girls' BMWs and Lexus cars
lined on the circular drive. I am probably the only girl whose mom
is dropping her off.

"Wow, *look at this house!*" Mom drags out.

"I'm looking at it." I mutter, gaping at the mansion. It probably
takes up a whole five acres—not counting the side lawn. How am I
supposed to just go up and ring the doorbell? I realize the sooner I
get out the better, so I quickly grab my clutch borrowed from Kelly
and step out of the car. "Thanks for driving me."

"Aw, of course Canzie! Have a blast!" She yells.

Late spring crickets and a wave of summer heat are overbear-
ingly distracting from the serenity of the fountain mist from the cul-
de-sac pond. I see a white BMW pull up behind us with a cheerleader
at the wheel. I slow my pace. Maybe I can walk in with whoever this
is and eliminate the awkwardness of walking in alone. But it looks
like that girl is actually waiting for me to walk in first, because she is
just sitting in her car for a good twenty seconds while I stand in the
middle of the road like a deer in headlights. *Why isn't mom driving
off?* I grunt, looking back at our dusty black suburban. Without waiting another second, I stand up straight and pray as I walk to the door.
God, please give me confidence as I walk into this party.

Ding-dong.

"Yes?" An affluent woman of middle age gracefully answers the
door. I can't help but feel as though she is analyzing every part of me;
from my worn-out suede sandals to my jean shorts all the way to the
frizzy baby hairs on top of my head.

"Hi, my name is Candice Gibbons and I'm, ugh…am a friend. Of Callie's."

"Oh?" The lady stands with a bewildered, yet kind look on her face. She is probably wondering what a tall, brown-headed girl is doing at her petite blond daughter's birthday party. It's not like she would recognize me from any pictures.

"I just moved here from Missouri." I add.

"I see. It is a pleasure to meet you. I am Callie's mother. Please, come in." She walks me through their hotel-like foyer. As I trail a little slower behind her, I can't help but notice just how luxurious this house is. The staircases alone look like they're from some classy richest-home-in-the-world magazine and everywhere I look are paintings and artifacts. I hear a quiet chatter in the kitchen as she escorts me through the first phase of the house: a modest, high ceiling parlor with fluffed pillows and bright windows overlooking a pool with a waterfall that curves around the edge of the west wing of the mansion. I assumed Callie was rich, but I had no idea it was like this. Thousands of butterflies fly back into my stomach when I realize I am the center of attention. As I walk in the kitchen, not only are most of the girls present and facing me, but everyone is undeniably dressed in cocktail party attire. Not one girl has on denim, and as my eyes search the bodies of teens, I realize they are all somewhat coordinate in fuchsia, cream, and jade cut-offs, while I feel like the Hunchback of Notre Dame because of this pink shawl that keeps falling off my left shoulder.

"Welcome to Carissa's 16th Birthday!" Mr. Winters raises his hand in gesture towards Callie and smiles the cheesiest grin. He resembles Callie's striking green eyes and defined jawline. All of the guests quickly flash a smile my direction as I approach the marble countertop they are leaning against. I still cannot believe I am invited to this party. I could not feel more out of place and thrilled.

"Welcome to the Winters's Estate, Candice!" Callie squeals. To my surprise, she is actually skipping towards me. She is wearing a colorful jumper that makes her tan look five shades darker.

"Happy birthday Callie! Thank you for inviting me!" I return the hug, hoping I don't sound desperate. Brooklyn Winters, Callie's beautiful older sister, leads us to snap pictures of us (or should I say Carissa and Callie) by the pool front. I spot Afton and Morgan and try to approach them, but they merely half-smile and turns to Carey, the junior cheerleader.

"Oh Cal, it's just horrible lighting back here, it must be from the balcony." Brooklyn cups a hand over her eyes. "Let's go to the west wing."

So, her entourage of girls follow her through their pebble-floored garage and past her black-rimmed BMW. "Isn't she gorgeous?" Callie says, leaning on the front of her brand-new car. She kisses it.

"Oh Callie, you're a big girl now!" Carissa squeals.

As we wrap up pictures, Claire pulls up and jumps out in a leather dress and dangly hoop earrings. "Hey ladies!" She smiles in her radiant way. Everyone is enthralled by her presence.

"Girl, I just love your look!" Everyone adores, running their hands down Claire's back and twirling her around. Then we, or should I say everyone but me, decides to snap a few more photos on the side of the house. And you won't believe it, but Callie actually asks to take a picture with me! Of course, when Brooklyn shows us how it turned out, I hate it, and Callie will probably delete it. But still! Now a decked-out party bus is swerving up the driveway. Lights are flashing from the inside and all the girls grab their wallets in a hurry.

"What a great idea Cal, a party bus to the Mediterranean cafe!"

"This is sick!" Everyone agrees upon boarding the bus. This year's hit releases are booming on the speakers, while everyone slowly and awkwardly finds a place on the long benches. At the sight of Callie's enthusiasm to dance to the music, I grow a little uncomfortable, remembering how they know I am a dancer, but I try to brush it off. This is such impure music, talking about love and breakups and everything. I am not sure if my presence at this party qualifies as being a "light" to OEH. You know that ladder illustration, where it is harder for you to pull someone up than it is for someone to pull you down? Well, here is proof.

We have been on the road for at least five minutes. Everyone seems to know the words to these explicit songs except me and a couple bashful freshmen. I do not want to seem rude that I am not joining in, because I already feel so out of place as it is. I adjust my cardigan back up on my shoulder to keep it from falling down my arm and smile for the sake of looking pleasant. Across from me sits Carey, boringly mature as always, and the freshmen cheerleaders who seem equally as uncomfortable is I am. Carey is in a short sky-blue dress and is sitting with straight posture, fiddling with one of her rings. I assume she is just as annoyed as I am for tolerating such music, but then I study her lips and notice she's quietly singing the words right along with them. And then I remember the ride in her car.

By the time we near the skyscrapers of OKC, the sun is setting, and all the girls are singing passionately and dancing disturbingly. *Oh no.* A chill shivers down my spine. *I forgot to get Mom's debit card! What am I supposed to do for food? Should I not eat?* I begin to panic, observe the many hands holding designer wallets full of unlimited cash, except for me. True, I brought my sister's wallet for show, but it is not like there is any cash in it I can use.

Frantically, I blow up Mom's phone with the hopes that she could discreetly bring me the card. Deep down I know she would not drive here just to do that, but this is a desperate situation. How foolish am I going to look at Callie Winters's birthday party having to ask for money! Sweat drips and my brow tightens as we turn the corner. We are dropped off on the side of the road and everyone downtown is staring at us like we are famous. I actually enjoy the attention of being in this group of popular girls. *But is this really what I want to be like?*

Mom texts back and assures me the parents will pay for it. But how am I supposed to know that? Thankfully, to my relief, I see that the Mr. and Mrs. Winters have seated themselves at the head of the table with margarita glasses in hand and I think we are safe. I am taking a discreet seat beside Afton and Carey, knowing they will probably ignore me most of the time anyway. Everyone seems to be high after that last inappropriate song in the car, but I am silently singing the lyrics to a worship song in an attempt to erase the horrible lyrics repeating in my mind. A nice summer breeze that has been present throughout this whole dinner is starting to turn cold. I notice Carey shiver in her skimpy dress.

"Hey Carey, want to wear my shawl?" I offer, trying to be like Jesus.

"Oh," she brushes off, scrunching her nose at my shawl, "I'm good, thanks anyway."

"No problem," I smile back. I know it isn't name-brand, but it is clothing.

Someone taps the edge of their glass. "Ladies, may I have your attention?" Mr. Winters says, "To my beautiful, wild, sarcastic, chipmunk Callie: May this year be full of love, friendship, pleasure, and adventure."

"Here, here!" Mrs. Winters raises her glass.

"To the birthday girl!" Brooklyn shouts as fifteen glasses rise in the air. A strong rush of wind startles all the shivering teens in their summer dresses, and I myself am feeling quite chilled even though I have my shawl; something they do not have. Once more I turn to Carey and offer her my cardigan.

"I said I'm fine." She snaps, but I see goosebumps on her pale, bony arms. I know better than to be offended.

"Look, we can share it. Here, let's put it on our legs." I remove my shawl which reveals my white tank and unaesthetically pleasing shoulders. Now, with my hair blowing behind me thanks to the wind, I am sure everyone's looking at my imperfect parts—like the faded blood clot on the side of my neck, or a surgical scar I have on my shoulder from a procedure related to my autoimmune disorder. But they're not. Carey is actually grateful for the extra covering on her legs, and I feel like God is smiling at me for reaching out.

As the night goes on, I am feeling more and more like I belong. It feels completely different than being in the party bus. Mr. and Mrs. Winters are fun and engaging, and my seat is directly across from Callie, so I am able to interact with her all night. Everyone is going around and supposed to share things they like about Callie. This wouldn't be so hard if I actually *knew* stuff about her. I mean,

I only have one class with her, and I can count on one hand how many conversations we have had at school. I don't even know her real birthday, let alone what qualities she has, not to mention I have zero memories that I could share.

It is almost my turn, and I am rummaging every corner of my brain for *something* positive to share. Her hair? Stunning. Her words? Um… Her actions? Well, I am not about to highlight that. *Why can't I have some hilarious story to share like Carissa and Claire just did?!*

"*My* favorite memory with Callie is when we went night swimming in California…"

"*My* favorite memory of Callie is when we won state for cheer in junior high…"

"I love Callie because she's just so kind and welcoming to everyone—so inclusive!"

So far, everyone sounds like robots repeating what the last person said: her beauty, academic achievements, cheerleading talent, and "fun times." Yet, these are all surface things. I am at a loss for words when it comes to talking about a popular girl and how she has influenced my life when I just met her four months ago. Afton is finishing her compliments, and everyone turns to me in slow motion. *God, please give me supernatural wisdom so I will not lie but can speak good qualities about Callie.*

"Callie, I haven't known you as long as all of these other girls have *(true)*, but it's clear that you are well loved and appreciated *(also true)*. From the first day I met you, you seemed happy and friendly *(all true things)* and over this past semester I've discovered you have a sensitive spirit towards the things of God *(I revert back to Bible class when she shared her testimony)*. You are kind and considerate…" I trail off with vague but applicable adjectives, "And whenever someone needs encouragement," I wrap my arm awkwardly around Carey for demonstration, "You go up to them and say, 'Do you need a hug?'" I hear an annoyed chuckle three seats down. I draw back my arm awkwardly again. "You are always making sure that everyone feels okay, and that's why people like you. I can't wait to see who you'll become someday, and I hope we have…many more memories in the future!"

The table falls silent, all eyes fixed on me. People are staring as if I am an angel or someone they have never heard speak before. I look down at my Mediterranean dish as a signal I am finished. *Okay, God. If you can use anything, use my words to point to you.*

After dinner, Mrs. Winters, wearing her Gucci belt and holding her phone to her ear is frantically searching for the party bus, which seems to have disappeared. Carissa and Callie are posing for pictures in front of a graffiti wall outside. Claire is in a corner to herself.

"How's it going Claire?"

"Eh..." she responds in her usual way, "I'm not one for taking pictures."

"You?" I gape in disbelief. But then I remember how Mika was so vulnerable, even when she seemed like the strongest girl in the room. "I'm not either," I chuckle, leaning against the wall and throwing my head back. It's so weird how seven months ago I was a different girl in a different world. None of these girls existed to me. But now, my world revolves around them every single day. Claire is a sophomore girl just like me, no matter how perfect she looks or acts, and she has problems just like the rest of us. I glance at Carey, then to the girls in the spotlight. My thoughts grow quiet. Did I really just announce that I "couldn't wait to make more memories with Callie?" Did that mean I was going to join cheer and stay at OEH?

"Bus is here, girls!" Mrs. Winters announces. The party bus is already jamming with deep base vibes. The sun has set, and the bus is much warmer than eating outside. It is dark and lit like a club. Callie leads the way by heading to the back of the bus and not sitting down, so we follow. As the bus driver revs up the engine and merges on the highway, I see Carissa flash an evil grin and hit play one of the dirtiest songs I have ever heard.

Girls can be sly, but you would never guess these OEH girls were low enough to dance *this* seductively. We are all girls here; can we not just dance respectfully? A few other girls seem to feel same as me, and we kind of sit back and let the dancers do their thing. I cannot help but feel a little uncomfortable with this overweight college dude driving the bus. Even realizing he's processing these descriptive lyrics makes me want to throw up.

He's got to be peeking back at us every once in a while. I think to myself, keeping a close eye on him. My eyes shift back to Carissa. Don't get me wrong, I like the energy of the room, but something about this makes me feel uneasy. I guess this is what they saw on TV growing up, so they are more than aware of how to act in this setting. I am glad I am not used to this.

"C'mon Claire! You're the pro dancer here, show us what you've got!" A voice shouts to my right. Claire shakes her head and backs away from the center.

"Yeah Claire, get in the middle!" Callie screams over the music.

"I don't know…" she hesitates, the smile disappearing from her face.

"Come on!" Carissa nags, and she begins pushing Claire in the center of the group.

I am sitting behind her on the top of the bench trying to decide if I should do something. *"She shouldn't have to do that."* I mumble. But I do not really know what to say to get her out of it. My hands are still robotically clapping to the music. Claire *is* a competitive dancer, so she is probably really good. And since I used to be a dancer, I would appreciate to see her talent. But not in this kind of setting. Not like this. *C'mon, Candice. Claire likes you! You can get her out of this situation!* I wrestle on the inside.

But before I know it, Claire is in the center against her will. I can tell by the look on her face she is a little uncomfortable, but she is getting more validation by the second. Everyone is oohs and ahhs make her feel like she is doing something right. I immediately feel sorry for her. I can tell she has a heart to do what is right, but when everyone around her is doing the opposite, she doesn't have any grit to overcome it.

"Ayyye!" The girls cheer as Claire ends her routine with a cheer kick.

"Hey Candice, you wanna hop in the center?" Callie asks.

"Noooooooo, thanks!" I smile and shake my head. Luckily, they are not expecting much from me anyway, and they move on to a freshman girl who is probably secretly happy they acknowledged her. During that split second all eyes were on me, I felt so special; something I don't feel on a regular basis at school. Are these my new group of girls I prayed God would send me? I glance at my reflection in the bus window. *I look like one of them tonight!* I think to myself. The truth is, I don't really *mimic* them. My shorts are all tucked up as I am sitting, and my hair is a little sweaty like theirs. My pink cardigan fell off my shoulder revealing my tank top during Claire's dance, but I have not fixed it yet. It feels kind of cool with the window being open and my shoulder exposed. It makes me feel powerful.

As the party bus rolls past the exit for OEH, something in me panics as if Mom and Dad are watching this right now with eyes are big as party bus wheels and faces as pink as my cardigan. Nobody is out on this part of town at this time of night, and it is kind of eerie. It is only 10:15 p.m. and it feels like we're the only people awake. Maybe it is because finals are still going on…

Finals! I have finals tomorrow! I panic, reaching for my phone to text Mom. Because I enrolled in two history classes this semester, I have an extra final while all these girls finished school today. I am sick with guilt thinking about how I have not studied a single thing for the final tomorrow. I have been so focused on all the others I finished today and getting ready for the party, and there is no time to think about this one. I text mom and tell her to come pick me up ASAP. She says it will be a good thirty minutes. *Just great.*

When we pull in the Country Club, everyone is calming down just a little bit. Afton has sweat dripping in her eyes and hair. Carissa's forehead is glistening in the strobe lights and Callie's fixing her jumper so it's not too revealing when she walks in the house. In Callie's eyes, I think the party was a success. I am even feeling a little flirty right now walking in with my shawl arm all hanging down and my eye makeup glossy with sweat. The last song's vulgar lyrics are stuck in my head, and I am too tired to think of another song to block them out.

"Thanks for driving us!" We pretty girls say to the driver as we exit the bus. We are back to being the fake polite girls they act like in school. The fresh whiff of outside air reminded me just how hot it was in the party bus. I kind of want to mess with the driver—just for the fun of it—and say something like, "*You didn't watch us the whole time, did you?*" And see his chubby face blush. I sort of feel sorry for this guy. If this is what he saw from Christian kids, why would he ever want to be a Christian?

I am sick I did not stand up for Christ.

"How was the party bus?" Mr. Winters asks, opening a box of macaroons on the kitchen counter.

"It was hot!" Morgan is sweating like she just ran a marathon. I see Claire standing beside Carey with a solemn smirk on her face. She is losing her innocence. I feel so angry at myself for not speaking up and giving Claire a way out of that situation. I mean, I would have hoped somebody would do that for me. I try to catch Claire's attention, but it is like she is avoiding me. Come to think of it, I think Claire admires my spiritual maturity. She has hinted this to me in the past. I hope I have not squandered her trust in me. I probably looked just like the rest of them on the bus, clapping and swaying to the music, even passively agreeing with them when they pressured Claire into dancing. If only I could go back and do it over…

Afton swaggers over to where I am standing and flashes her usual "I'm so annoyed" cheesy smile. I used to think she was being sarcastic with me, but now I realize she does this to everyone. "You wanna split one of the giant chocolate macaroons?" She asks.

A macaroon is the last thing I need right now. I have already stuffed myself with a double helping of Mediterranean pasta tonight, and our final track meets are coming up. Yet, I don't have anything else to do for the next thirty minutes. "Yeah, let's do it!" The words spill out of my mouth before I have time to think about this too deeply. Brooklyn is telling us about life as a college student while I cut the macaroon in half and grab two silver forks on the counter. Carissa and Callie are having their own side conversation that looks super exclusive, while Carey and Morgan are listening in. Afton is eying me to make sure I cut the cookie evenly. It is nearing 10:40 p.m. and some of the girls are starting to leave. At least I am not the first one, although I am starting to feel the pressure of the track meet coming up. I give the basketball girls hugs and wish them well. Morgan does not smile, just returns a half-hearted embrace and jingles her keys as she walks away. It is like she silently communicated that she liked me. It feels so good to be liked! I want to make sure to have a moment with each of the cheerleaders so I can leave feeling like I conquered it—like I have their approval. I am feeling quite certain this is the group God wants me to spend the rest of high school with, even if I have some different convictions. It is not like they do drugs or anything.

To my relief, the long-awaited >*Here!*< text from Mom pops up on my phone. I am surprised to see just how much of the macaroon I ate while making small talk. My stomach is no longer filled with imaginary butterflies, but another plateful of unhealthy carbs.

When I announce I am leaving, I am pleased to see Callie and Claire jump up from where they are sitting and give me hugs. Even Carissa stops her conversation and hugs me.

"We were all thinking we should have a bonfire or something this summer together!" She says in her usual enunciated valley girl voice. *Did I really just get invited to hangout again by Carissa Carlyle?* I wonder in fascination.

Without skipping a beat, I pretend this is not a surprise. "Oh, that would be so much fun!" And before I realize what's happening, I voice my thoughts: "It's so funny to think that last December we just met, and you walked in the office and introduced yourself to me..."

"Oh, my goodness, yes!" She carries on, and we actually reenact our awkward handshake. A few other girls are crowded around listening. It is a little surreal to think that I used to fear their clique. Now, I am truly accepted.

Carissa and I hug again, and I run upstairs into Callie's bedroom. Carey is in here charging her phone as I grab my bag of unused swim clothes.

"Ugh, my dad is saying I need to come home so I can be back by my curfew." She complains, leaning against Callie's bed. "Seriously,

I am a junior." She adds, dropping her phone on the floor. I silently pray that God would give me an opportunity to connect with her.

"Yeah, I am having to leave now too. I have got my Oklahoma History final tomorrow."

"Oh, that stinks." She says. But before I can say anything else, Callie marches up and starts a conversation with Carey. I feel a little awkward standing in between them with this old bag over my shoulder, so I begin my farewells. Callie reaches up and I bend down as we embrace, and she seems genuinely glad that I attended her party. I am too.

Mrs. Winters escorts me out the door and says the usual *thank-you-for-coming yadayadayada* speech while she opens the door.

"It was a pleasure, Mrs. Winters." I flash a Candice smile and stepping onto the porch. As the door closes, a wave of relief lasts a good five seconds as I soak in these last few moments of victory. *I am in one of the richest neighborhoods in town, standing on Callie Winters's porch!* I whisper out loud. I walk to Big Roy no longer feeling like the insecure girl who stepped out a few hours ago. Someone's headlights flash on me as I run behind the car, and I quickly open the passenger seat door to escape whoever can see me.

Lo and behold, Kelly is also sitting inside wearing her cranberry star-speckled pajamas. I hastily shut the door and hop in the backseat beside my little brother's car seat.

"Please drive quickly." I say to Mom, who is in pajamas herself.

"Woah, there, hasty Canzie! Slow down! How was it?!" Mom turns around and smiles at me. Where do I even begin?

"It was definitely a…party." I quickly cover my shoulder with my drooping shawl. My mind replays flashbacks of seeing the inside of their house, the music playing in my head, and the seductive dancing in the bus. Then, I think about what just happened when Carissa and I had a connection, and people hugging me when I left. That was insane.

"Did you survive?" Mom asks, probably thinking about how nervous I was to go to this party.

"Oh, I survived." I say back, "I actually had a lot of fun."

"Aw yay, Canzie! I'm so happy for you!" She congratulates. "I brought Kelly to show her the Country Club."

"Yeah, this place is nice." I say, trying to divert attention away from me. We pass the lake and golf course and drive out of the gated community without saying anything. I lean my head on the window and sigh. I am thinking about everything I witnessed and learned tonight about the world: Callie's family and home, the kind of music these girls know, and the style of dance they performed. Is all this really the life God intended for us to live?

Ironically, Mom seems to be reading my thoughts. "You think these girls are your people?"

I bite my lip. I really think I *could* be like them. Once I get my license this fall, I would be driving just like they are. I have already been accepted in their friend group. But then I think about my gut feelings going into this. Am I seriously turning into *one of them?* The girls that exclude the other kids from their lunch table? The clique that makes a circle the hallways and gossips about 'less than' students?

"I don't know, Mom." I finally say, undoing my sandals and propping my feet up in the car seat. I gaze at my reflection in the window, glowing from the moonlight. *Should I officially click with this clique?*

"No." My grandmother Annie's words on the other end of the phone hit me like a punch in the gut. A good punch. Like the kind you know is coming and you readily deserve. Still, it hurts all the same.

"You don't think all I just experienced is a sign that God's making a way for me to be a part of the popular crowd?"

"It's definitely an opportunity," she cautions, "but sometimes doors open like a test to see if you'll walk through them or not. Just because a door opens, if doesn't mean you're supposed to walk through it."

"But...but..." I stammer. "I thought this was my blessing from all the sacrifices I experienced this semester. You know, my reward for moving to Oklahoma."

"Remember when you told me your first reaction to the cheer-leaders' personalities? You said they were stuck up and cliquish."

"But that was before I got to know them! They're not half as bad close up…" I immediately regret saying. A flashback of Carissa and I shaking hands replays in my mind.

"Oh Candice, don't lose your identity in the wrong crowd just because they're the first ones to offer you a seat at the table. Don't you trust that God will bring you the right friends?"

"These might *be* them, Annie!" I plead back, but on the inside, as painful as it may be to choose to be lonely once again, I know what I have to do.

Chapter Thirteen

JUNTOS

FINALS WERE A breeze. A classy, Chanel perfume breeze. Even my math grade was decent. I walk the halls unashamed as a trendsetter—a popular girl—riding on the highs of the party. And yet, I know what I need to do. I scan the cafeteria for the cheerleaders to see if they decided to eat on campus, because no one texted me about going out for lunch. Everyone seems to have gone to Parsley Bowl and forgotten about me. And I am okay with that.

"Hi," I set my tray down next to Isabelle at the awkward kids' table. Mabrey is shocked to see me here, especially after rumors about Callie's party have circulated the school. "It's okay if I sit here, right?"

"Of course, it is!" Mabrey defends out of nowhere.

"She was at Callie Winters's party." Isabelle scowls at me.

Isabelle scoots closer to the edge like I have the popular girls' disease.

"How did your finals go?" I turn to the nerdy-looking boy sitting across from me, who's slurping a soggy plate of baked beans.

"Huh?" He peers up from his science fiction novel with a bewildered face.

"Your finals. How did they go?"

"Oh, ugh…they were good." He stammers with a little boy smile. And then it hits me this kid isn't a sophomore, but a freshman who happens to be in my math class. How could I not have recognized him? I was too engulfed with my own problems to see anyone else.

"Wasn't that math final a pain?" I say with wide eyes. Isabelle and Mabrey eye me curiously.

"He's a freshman," Mabrey whispers in my ear. I nod and smile unmoved.

"Yeah, they were." The nerdy boy says finally.

"I doubt I even passed!" I say proudly.

"Huh?" Isabelle interjects.

"Like, does anyone understand Algebra?" I say to the table. "Yeah, guys. I am in Algebra."

Everyone gasps except Mabrey and the nerdy boy.

"Honestly, I doubt I will pass this class either." The boy sits a little straighter. "I may be a sophomore in it next year just like you were."

"Welcome to the club!" I laugh. But my joy quickly subsides. There they are: the *entire* cheer team is entering the cafeteria as if in slow motion. Each one of the Carissa's friends' eyes are fixed on me, as if I have just blown my entire chance of becoming a popular girl. Carissa whispers to Callie something I am certain is about me, but I simply stare at them with an intentionally unfazed look, smiling ever so slightly before turning to Mabrey. God has given me a peace about being kind to everyone, including, but not limited to, the cheerleaders. It is time to tear down this horrible sophomore clique culture. It is time for everyone to learn from everyone. I think my role as a light is officially happening. Right now.

"So, I heard you're on the swim team!" Climactic symbols clash in my head.

"Ugh, yeah." Mabrey says, glancing at the cheerleaders and then back at me. "Look, if you want to leave and go with your friends, you can. It looks like you have your first choice back for a lunch table." She adds in a lower voice.

"No," I say, right as the wind of Carissa's miniskirt blows past me. "I'm good."

Mabrey gapes at me and then swallows her own air.

"So, you're on the swim team…" I continue our conversation. This makes Isabelle and Mabrey smile, and Mabrey goes on to share how terrible the OEH swim team is, but how she beat her times from last year and may even receive a college scholarship. We then relate summer plans and how crazy it is that we will be juniors next year. And then a still, small voice whispers something in my heart. I am almost certain it is God speaking, nudging me forward.

"Mabrey, I know you probably have your own church you attend, but if you ever wanted to come with me, we have this really cool youth group that meets every Wednesday night. This coming week, we're having a talent show, and you are welcome to sit by me."

"Really?" She peers at me. "You'd…you'd be surprised at how many students *don't* invite others to their churches out of assumption that everyone goes to church. But I'm not really connected to my youth group…"

"Really?"

"Yeah," she bites into her ham sandwich and wipes her mouth with a napkin. "I'll give you my number."

And so, I go on to tell her about Tia and the youth leaders that are at church, and how the youth pastor's messages hit the hard topics. "It's really cool," I say. Even by inviting my first person to church, I feel as if it has connected me to New Life even more. I heard somewhere that everyone is deficient in encouragement. Never underestimate the power of an invitation.

Once I finish my lunch, I excuse myself and walk to throw it away, passing the druggie table. An empty spot between one of Keli's ex-boyfriends and Allister remains consistent ever since she left. I try not to cry. "Hey," I say, sliding on the edge of the bench. Kenny and Allister just stare at me with bleak faces. Keli's ex-boyfriend won't bother to look up.

"I miss her." I say solemnly. "I just wish I could have had one more chance to talk with her."

No one says anything.

"I just wanted to say…I'm sorry for not hanging out with you guys more."

Keli's ex-boyfriend locks eyes with me. "We don't need sympathy from a cheerleader."

"She's not like them." Allister speaks up. "Keli and Candice were really close."

I bite my lip. "I get it." As I stand to throw away my tray, I hear someone call my name across the cafeteria.

"Candice!" I recognize Claire's melodic voice. I feel a knot in my stomach from what happened last night. Here is another person I let down.

"Hey," I say as cheerfully as I can.

"I just wanted to say, um…I really like you, and I hope we can keep in touch this summer, even outside of," she eyes Carissa cautiously, "the group."

"Really?"

"That is, if you want to…" she plays with her diamond necklace.

"I would love that!" I beam, and then Carissa screams her name from the popular table.

"Duty calls." She rolls her eyes, waving at me and running towards Carissa's voice.

It is her life, not mine, and I can finally rest in that. I am excited to get to know Claire for who she is, not just what she looks like or what she does. At homecoming, at Callie's party, there were moments of compromise: do I sing the lyrics to this song? Should I dance like everyone else? In the moment the pressure seemed so intense. But stepping back, it all looks so foolish. I cannot say that I vow never to be tempted to join in with people who do wrong, because I am human, and I will face temptations for the rest of my life. But I do know this: I was not wrong for not joining in. It may have felt unfamiliar or nerve-wracking, but that does not mean what I sensed was just introverted naivety.

I read in Romans, "Don't participate in the darkness of wild parties and drunkenness, or in sexual promiscuity and immoral living, or in quarreling and jealousy. Instead, clothe yourself with the presence of the Lord Jesus Christ. And don't let yourself think about ways to indulge your evil desires" which pretty much sums up my question on whether it was right to dance. And not everyone agrees with me on this, some people might not feel convicted doing certain things, like Claire, but that is okay. Because I can only control myself, and someday I will stand before God and be held responsible for everything I ever did.

"Yay! Mexican for dinner!" Jordan shouts at the dinner table.

"I like enchiladas, but the queso is my favorite." Kelly stretches her wrists and closes her homework books as Bria sets the table. Kelly and I are used to quickly turning around our homework space at the table to eat dinner, seeing as though the space is used for both activities.

"Candice, clean up your stuff." Mom tells me as everyone bows their head to pray.

God, please help me come up with a music video idea for Journalism class. Fast. I pray silently at the end of our dinner prayer.

And then idea hits me.

"Can someone drive me to a Mexican restaurant tomorrow?" I blurt out.

"What?" Dad asks, rubbing his heart.

"I need to film a music video for Journalism."

"At a Mexican restaurant?" Allison questions.

"Actually, I am going to need to go to a few locations. I'll explain later. So, Mom or Dad, can you?" Everyone stares at me silently. Finally, to my surprise, both Mom and Dad agree to drive me around over the weekend. And while I am still not quite certain where this music video is going, my inner creativity is escalating back to its normal high level. I am ready to break out.

"This is depressing." Stella laments in the locker room.

Today is very sad, indeed. It is our last track practice of the season. All the memories of bus rides, grueling practices, and late-night ice cream celebrations after a track meet, all of it will be ending in a matter of days.

"I don't know where this semester went," says Emma solemnly.

"Me neither," agrees Kinsley, changing into her shorts and tank top.

"At least we have the track banquet to look forward to," Mika reminds us. "And by then, all of our finals will be finished, including our Journalism music videos, Candice."

"Music videos?" Stella laughs in her deep, athletic voice. "What's yours about Mika?"

"Oh, just some clips thrown together of senior year memories... What I am *really* excited to see is Candice's music video!"

"What's yours about?" Emma asks me.

"Oh," I blush, throwing my hair into a ponytail. "I did mine to a Latino song and dressed up in a sombrero. I am basically mouthing words I don't know the whole time." I am not thrilled with how it turned out, I am just more thankful I finished it and I overcame situational depression. I made Mrs. Lajuana a promise to finish it, and I worked really hard on the editing of it last weekend.

"Candice in a sombrero? This I gotta to see!" Kinsley smirks.

"She's a really good journalist." Adds Mika.

"All students are required to attend the schoolwide assembly next Monday, May 21ˢᵗ at 5:00 p.m. Parents are welcome to come." Principal Vanderbilt replaces Mrs. Gray's usual voice on the loudspeakers. *What is this about?*

"Wow...Allister. What an...enlightening video of how to not park your car." Mrs. Lajuana tries to stay composed, handing Allister a tiny Journalism trophy for "Most Unique Video." "Next up is Candice Gibbons." Mrs. Lajuana clicks her computer and suddenly a huge blown up visual of me wearing a fake mustache and sombrero is on the projector. The class is laughing hysterically. Even Mika.

"This will be interesting." The baseball boy says to his friend. My heart races like a thoroughbred throughout the five-minute video. Now that I watch it displayed on this screen, the editing isn't half bad, but no one seems to be paying attention to my video skills. Everyone is laughing at me. I am the class joke.

Not you too! I see Mrs. Lajuana surprising giggles form her desk. Her hand is covering her mouth and her eyes are sparkling with happy tears. When the video ends with me almost getting hit by a car (Mom was the driver) everyone laughs even harder. Mika even walked across the room to pat me on the shoulder. "You made my day."

"Wow. That was…unbelievable!" Mrs. Lajuana says when it ends. "I am *highly* impressed." She stammers. And then everyone claps for me three times more than anyone else.

"Congratulations, Candice. You receive the award for Most Passionate Journalism Student!" She hands me a tiny trophy.

"Thank you, thank you." I smile, taking a bow before the class. My confidence has risen a hundred miles high. Not because of their applause, but more out of the accomplishment I feel for finishing this video and making Mrs. Lajuana proud. What was disguised as a burdensome video project, God used as a runway.

Slowly but surely, my leadership and creative gifts are creeping out into the open. It's as if they were buried under my insecurities starting a new school and comparing my life to others. Now, I feel accomplished, yet genuine. I am not itching to be a cheerleader. I am not dying to win a track medal. I am simply being the best version of myself. Like I am finally embracing who God wanted me to be in Oklahoma—the same girl who lived in Missouri but was challenged and matured. To think that I almost skipped out on life altogether!

Chapter 14

MEDALS AND MEMORIES

B US FUMES LEAK as anticipation mixes with grogginess and
settles over us. Me, Mika, and Stella are boarding the bus for
our final track meet. We are matching in black sweatshirts
over red jerseys, our Nike sweatpants over our running shorts. No
one says anything because the hour is too sweet; too early. Even for
me, a morning person, my eyelids burn. When you wear contact
lenses, you cannot just take them in and out. I call it an eye reset.
You have to give them some time to breathe while you are awake.
Otherwise, you wake up with Exhibit A: me right now. But I did not
do an eye reset. It was a late night of journaling.

But here we are, contacts back in again, and I am looking for a
place to sit on the bus. All the track boys—mostly skinny, some big
and muscular, each particularly hairy and disorganized, and some are
clutching turtle stuffed animals and basketball-themed pillowcases—
smelling like oily hair mixed with cologne. Since they are stretching
over bench seats and blocking the way, I just hop over their out-
stretched legs and move to a solitary seat mid-way on the left, gluing
myself to the window so I can warm up and watch the continuing
line of half-awake highschoolers shuffle to the bus. Once I realize

how many people are behind me, I hold my breath as the thought occurs, I must share a seat with somebody.

The bench across is occupied by Janner Trey, a charismatic goofball wearing a blue fishing hat and stuffing a red OEH duffle bag under the seat. I see Zach Bernard, whom we call Bernard, another junior with beach blond hair and a manly face saving a spot next to him on the very back bench. As captain of the team, Mika sits near Coach Stanley at the front of the bus. Stella joins another freshman. Out the window, to my right, I spot Jaden Smith the junior, the missing piece to his puzzle. She is carrying a pillow and a blanket, along with a collection of Under Armour bags. As she nears the bus, I dread the thought of having to share a seat with a boy—or worse—a freshman. The seats are filling up around me with game-faced athletes. I feel like the intruder tagging along in my oversized sweatshirt to capture this story (and in a way, I am). To my relief, Emma is getting aboard and catches my eye. "Hey Candice, can I sit with you?"

"Yeah!" It hits me she is probably sitting with me closer to the back just to be here with the guys, but I do not mind. It is someone who will either completely ignore me, or someone who I would be thrilled to talk to. Jaden is now entering the back of the bus, deciding to jump in through the emergency exit and slip beside Bernard. He curls his muscular arm around her shoulder and smiles, as she wraps the blanket around their shoulders and buries her face in his chest. Their fairytale ends there.

"Absolutely not!" Yells Coach Stanley from the driver's seat. "You two cannot sit all cozy together in the back seat! Get out, now." So, Jaden, tall, and moving like a gymnast, tucks her hair behind her ear and moves grudgingly up a few rows to hog her own bench.

Emma is now sitting beside me snuggled in a scarlet, fuzzy blanket. She is seventeen and acts like it, about my height, with a deep olive tan, bright green eyes, and a beaming dimpled smile. Her hair, practically the same shade as her skin, is brown and straight and thick. Her voice is deep and down-to-earth toned, glazed with humor and calmness. Emma *does* talk to me, and even if it is about shallow topics like what I ate for breakfast, who cares! I have a friend who is older than me. "I don't even want to be awake right now."

"Aw." I sympathize, then branch out, "Can I have some blanket too?"

"Yeah!"

"Thanks, I think I might sleep, too." I relate. "It's hard to sleep on buses."

"I have like three tests whenever I get back."

"Why did they do that to you after the junior retreat?"

"I don't know…" she turns to the boys who are routing our trip.

"It says like 53 minutes. I was hoping it would be like 2 minutes."

"I brought oranges. I brought some cuties for you…you cuties." Janner says. He is awkward and proud of it. We laugh.

"Yeah, I don't feel like running." Emma groans.

"Yeah, I am not ready." I say. "If they were to put me out there to run right now, I would like just stand there, like 'wha?'"

"I would just like push over all their hurdles." She laughs then turns to the boys. Their words are hysterical—they don't make sense.

"It's gonna be so nice today. Yeah, it's going to be so nice."

"I can't wait to get my track tan."

"Who the heck is that? Is that Kinsley?"

"It's because she's the soccer babe."

"Janner, is she fast?"

"She's fast for a soccer girl."

"What do I always call soccer? What do I always tell you soccer is?"

"It's a gateway sport."

"It's a gateway sport."

"They started pulling my leg hair and I was like…"

"Janner. No way."

"That's dedication."

'Dude, you're insane!"

"My mom's a dental hygienist and she does everything, and she was like, 'Your teeth are crooked and—'"

"I got hit in the face with a hockey stick at one time and it chipped my tooth in half. I…I caught it whenever it flew out. It was weird."

"I was like...at first, I grabbed Bernard and I was like...no for real."

"Yeah, our leg hair."

"Okay, shhh...guys, I need to think about the 800-meter."

"I need that."

"The 800-meter?!"

Pulling up to the track meet we do what we always do: unload the high jump poles and chocolate milk ice-packed coolers and tent bags from the bus, look for a shady spot near the track to watch the events and hunker down. It is cold and wet on the grass from last night's rain, and I love it. We got rained out of a track meet once. I got to skip the dreaded 400-meter. We ended up going to McAllister's for sandwiches.

This spring, nearly every Saturday has been marked by a track meet. And even if I do not have a particular friend, I love watching the dynamics and interactions of everyone. Plus, I relish the immediate opportunities to quickly improve upon my 400-meter race time. But this particular track meet is sad because it is my last one to date, the last time I will get to ride the bus as an athlete, have a three-digit number Sharpied on my hand, and set up blocks on the track before my 100-meter dash. It is really quite sad. Moments like this welcome the nostalgia of the past...

Tecumseh, Oklahoma, was where I had my first 'away' track meet, not at OEH. A bunch of last-minute additions to the team came along, and a boy brought his boom box, and we turned up loud rap music and all squished together to take pictures and tell stories and share snacks. One parent brought us a whole charcuterie board of grapes, cheddar cheese chunks, and strawberries, also offering us homemade chocolate pretzels wrapped in plastic bags. The reason she brought this snack is because chocolate, like chocolate milk, is supposed to help your muscles recover after strenuous exercise. And salt, of course, helps your body maintain water and keep your heart rate up. At race time, I shaved a full 8 seconds off the previous week's 400-meter race time. I watched a girl fall and bust up her knee while running the 100-meter race—making me not get last—but I felt really bad for her, especially when blood went everywhere, and it turned out she needed stitches.

We had a track meet on the college campus of Oklahoma Baptist University, or OBU, which was exceptionally different. There were college kids facilitating the meet, and the restrooms were nice because they were not in some outdoor locker room, but in the building of their athletic center. My dad came to that track meet. He wore his long sleeve bright green hoodie with matching neon tennis shoes, sitting on the bleachers with an umbrella, sunglasses, and a hat to keep from getting sunburned. It was *so* hot. Mika's boyfriend offered us all massages. Stella and were grossed out. Dad said I looked so tall and strong—like the leader of the pack—when I walked on the track to run. My willpower is stronger than my ability, and you cannot buy that. I learned to be strong through practices in both rain and shine. I ran one of my worst times at OBU, but I was happy. I blame my time on the heat.

My favorite track meet was in Bristow, Oklahoma. It was in the middle of nowhere. The colors of the school were purple and white. The track was black and very old, cracking like crusty bread. There was only one side of bleachers. A tractor was parked in the grass lot beside the buses. It felt oddly similar to Ozark, and I half expected to see my friends' cars to drive by and cheer me on. Coach Lakyn was unable to make it, but Coach Stanley was in a tremendously wonderful mood. He kept giving us high-fives and fist bumps and jokes to keep us in good spirits. "Coach Lakyn keeps me serious," he would say, tying his school sweatshirt tightly around his head until all you could see were his pilot sunglasses. He is much more casual outside of OEH, wearing all school sports gear and trashing the professor attire. And I think he gets a kick out of my nerve to even be here.

"What are you reading?" Emma is asking, and I realize I have been holding my book upside down while recounting past memories.

"Oh, ugh, it is called *Autopilot: The Art and Science of Doing Nothing.*"

I have a habit of bringing along a complicated textbook on random trips and track meets, probably subconsciously to impress people when I am in a socially anxious setting. I don't recommend this, because when they ask you about it, like right now, you better at least understand it. But I have not matured in this area yet, and I have done it for a while now. Like on the missions trip I went on last spring, bringing along a book about the DNA regions of the brain. But actually, I find *Autopilot* not entirely complicated, and I start to highlight some of the text. Science has not been my strong suit, so I must work extra hard at it. "It's about…the art and science of doing nothing." I reread the subtitle.

"Cool," Emma says, leaning her back against her backpack. Mika is reading an Asian book about massage therapy. The boys are on their phones.

"All girls running the 100-meter dash, please go to the heating benches." The stadium speaker booms. Stella and I rise and dust off pretzel crumbs from our sweatpants.

"You've got this, girls!" Emma claps her hands.

"Go kill 'em!" Mika adds. "Show them what OEH can do!"

We saunter onto the inner field of the track with our shoulders bowed up, a competitive scowl mixed with a victorious smile. At the heating benches, we tell our name, grade, and school to the volunteer, who writes on our wrists a three-digit number in sharpie pen, numbers I have come to cherish. Then we are told to give our times. The fastest girls run together in the first heat—the first race—and then they work their way down. I am in one of the last heats.

"Can you hold my blocks for me?" Stella asks, and so I lie down on the track, bracing my feet against the metal starting blocks. Stella does her signature jump twice, shake three times, floss-your-arms circuit before pressing her fingers to the bumpy ground (it hurts more than you think) and propping her feet in the blocks.

And while she does this, I can't help but think that I have gotten it all wrong.

I never thought I was included in track. I thought I was a floater, an average kid in class, a gothic girl at lunch, an invisible runner in the afternoon, and a cheerleader on the weekends. I thought the track girls detested having a slow runner on the team. After all, they rarely spoke to me. I was the last place, last chance resort. But now I see athletes, at least like Stella, think differently: their actions speak louder than words. Stella asked me to hold her blocks, and we usually walk together to go to the bathroom. Mika has talked with me after practice, and even acknowledges me in the halls sometimes. Emma sat with me on the bus and cared enough to ask about the book I was reading. They *do* care, they have showed me their friendship consistently.

Bang! Stella is off to the races, winning first place in the first heat.

Bang! Candice is off to the races. I win fourth place in the last heat.

Bang! The OEH relay team is off: Stella as the runner of the first leg, Emma as second, Kinsley as third, and Mika as the anchor. They are fast and they win.

Our boys' team is disqualified because Zach dropped the baton. The mood on the bus ride home is 'defeated,' despite the girls' victories. Zach was so fast, he should have won, and the boys are understandably upset. The night is hot and Oklahoma-humid. It is drizzling with rain, and we smell like what we look like—a bunch of sweaty teenagers. The girls and I are quietly chatting and sharing bags of salty popcorn and goldfish. Coach Stanley is singing a country love song to himself, and Coach Lakyn is gripping a hand-sized foam roller and massaging Bernard's sore calf muscle. He looks like he is crying.

"Hey lousy team," Coach Stanley yells from the front, "How 'bout we all go to Buffalo Wild Wings?"

"Really, Coach?"

"I'm in!"

"Let's go!"

I recall the concept that everyone is deficient in encouragement.

The restaurant is in what feels like the middle of nowhere, but it is heavily occupied. Our tall, black-clad group shuffles in like we just lost a fight. The girls and I order parmesan wings and talk about our favorite parts of the season, and afterwards, we walk over to Braum's next door for ice cream sundaes. Kinsley and Jaden order a large toffee sundae, and they let me take a picture of them. We laugh over

Coach Stanley's quotes of the day and help each other finish eating the dishes. It is true bonding, and I am overflowing with happiness.

"Thank you to all of the parents for supporting this lousy track team throughout the season." Coach Stanley strokes his mustache, looking quite eccentric in his bowtie and suspenders. He stands before a banquet setting of wealthy couples and their athletic children in suits and dresses. My parents are here too, dressed in their modest church clothes, periodically waving to me from a corner table in the shadows of the banquet hall. I would be sitting with them, but Mika invited me to sit beside her at a table with Emma, Kinsley, and Stella.

"There's a lot of warm fuzzies from Coach." Stella rolls her eyes.

"Yeah, I never knew how much he loved us." Emma laughs. I fiddle with the silky fabric of my black dress and smile. To think I used to be intimidated by these upperclassmen, but now I see their just girls like me. Emma and Kinsley even invited me to sit beside them on the bus at our last track meet, and they asked me questions about Ozark! Never in a million years would I have thought a track girl would ask me about my hometown. Obviously, God is blessing me.

"You're totally going to win an award tonight." Kinsley winks at Mika. "You ran the best times in the whole state!"

"Yeah, Mika. You were amazing!" Adds Emma.

"You know what I loved most about you, Mika?" I speak up, and all heads turn to me.

"What?" Mika tilts her head of tight brown curls to the side and smiles in her gentle manner.

"Your confidence. You never shied away from a challenge. Remember the meet in Bristow where those boys were picking on one of our freshman boy runners? You shut down their party so fast their heads were spinning!"

"Yeah, Mika. Everyone knows you're the boss around here. It's going to be weird when you're off at college next semester." Emma adds.

Mika's face is radiant with joy. "Wow, thanks guys!"

"...And that's why this year's Top Track Runner on the girls' team goes to Mika McClain!" Coach Stanley hits perfect timing with his announcement.

"*Woohoo!*"

"*Go Mika!*"

"*Yeah, girl!*" Our table erupts with whistles and applause. Mika totally deserves her award. I am so thankful we became friends. When I first arrived at OEH, I automatically wrote her off in a "no-way-we'd-be-friends" kind of a way, only because she was older and popular and beautiful. But like I misconceived with the cheerleaders, she's just a senior. Someday I'll be a senior just like her, and I hope I will make an impact on younger girls in my life.

"And for our final award for the girls' team...*achem...*" coach Stanley coughs into the microphone. "Someone who worked extremely hard this track season. She's always had a great attitude and runs the 400 pumping her first in the air when she's halfway around the track...even though she's usually in last place."

Wait a minute...

"This person has been the positive encourager to the team. Through every single race she has improved..."

Kinsley looks at me with a smirk.

Surely, it's not...

"The Heart and Soul Award is going to someone who you would have never picked to be a runner."

Laughter fills the room. Now it is clear: he is talking about Candice Gibbons.

"*It's you!*" Mika mouths at me.

"And that girl is...*Candice Gibbons!*" Coach Stanley exclaims.

"*Yay!*"

"*Go Candice!*"

"*Woohoo!*" Everyone yells. Without wasting a second, I walk humbly up to the front of the room, bowing slightly to receive the blue and silver medal engraved with my name. And then, facing the audience, I smile and thank them. If only everyone knew how much I have overcome to earn this moment. If only they knew of my foot surgery and how I stopped dance and my blood pressure issues. If they only knew of the depression I fought and my struggle to even want to live. But God knew. And He honored me for it! I may not be the fastest runner on the track, or ever be able to dance again, but I have learned the invaluable lesson of hard work.

"What did I tell you?" I hold the medal up to my dad's camera after the track banquet, beaming with pride. "I won a track medal! *Me, Candice!*"

Dad shakes his head in disbelief. "I can't believe it, Candy Cane. You earned it! And Coach Stanley tells me your times for the 400 were shaved down by eight seconds over the season!"

"She's a hard worker, that one." Coach Stanley approaches us, smoothing his oily hair. "You deserve that medal."

"Thanks, Coach." I give him a hug.

"You don't have to run ever again. You've already proved to yourself you can do it." Mom says when he walks away. "You…"

"Oh, hold on a minute, Mom…"

Mika is twirling her keychain and walking towards the doors. I have to catch her before she leaves—it may be the last time I ever see her. "Mika! Wait up!" I yell.

She turns around. "Congratulations, Candice!"

"Congrats to you as well!"

"I guess we both can relax now that our Journalism videos are turned in and track is over." She smiles halfheartedly.

"Yeah," I nod. "Hey, before you leave, I just wanted to say thank you for being a role model to me throughout this semester. It was really hard leaving Missouri and going to a private school for the first time. I had no idea how much it would wreck my life. *It's a lot of pressure going to OEH…*" I add in a whisper.

"Tell me about it," she widens her eyes.

"I feel like I am coming out of one of the hardest seasons of my life full of confidence. I drifted from reading the Bible and praying, but once I started to do that again, it's like all of the puzzle pieces of my life started fitting together."

"That's cool!" She exclaims. "And a good reminder for me to stay close to God when I go off to college this fall."

"Yeah! I'll be praying with you on that. And I won't keep you any longer, I just wanted to say thank you for talking to me and believing in me, and I hope I am half as good as you when I am a senior."

"Hey, you're already way cooler than I'll ever be." She punches me in the shoulder playfully. "You're a born leader. Keep being you!" She waves while she walks off.

"I will!" I wave back.

"You heard what I said, right?" Mom asks me in the car.

"About not running track? Yeah, well, the problem is, I feel like I can't stop *now*." I smile with adrenaline. "Not after I've come so far. My feet may not be healed, but I haven't died yet. And if God can help me run track this year, He can help me again, right?"

"Absolutely." Dad chimes in. "I think what Mom is trying to say is not to be unwise. Take care of yourself."

"Oh, I will." I promise, leaning my head against the back of the seat. But I have already decided what I am going to do—there's nothing else I *can* do—I am determined to sign up for track next spring and beat my records.

"Candice! Come sit over here!" Claire calls to me above the noise at the school-wide assembly. Ironically, she is sitting next to Mabrey and a girl from drama class, and everyone seems to be enjoying themselves. This is the first time I don't sense myself being pulled into a clique, and I really like this feeling. I readily slide in the aisle seat next to Claire. It is as if we have made our own little group: me, Claire, and Mabrey—someone from each 'clique.' The only one missing is Keli.

Oklahoma Excellence's auditorium has high marble walls that make everyone's voices echo. The stage is festooned with thick, wine-red curtains and a row of teachers standing proudly in the shadows.

The seats are decorated with suit-and-tie young men scattered among prim and proper girls in their chapel dresses and curled hair in velvet red chairs. Delighted parents eye their star children from the parent section in the balcony, with cameras positioned to video their son or daughter win an award.

Principal Vanderbilt proceeds to congratulate all the students who have exceeded the average mold of a typical student and have set the bar for future generations of leaders. Claire's name is called for the of OEH's Outstanding Sophomore Scholar Award and I catch a glimpse of Carissa's darkened face as Claire passes her aisle on her way to the stage. Carissa has been cordial but undoubtedly her old self. And while I believe we could continue to be cordial to one another throughout the remaining years of high school, I won't ever fall for the popularity trap again. Claire, on the other hand, is on the verge of turning a new leaf. I can feel it. As she shakes hands with Principal Vanderbilt in her pearl white heels and pencil dress, her demeanor is humble, yet graceful. Mabrey and I applaud loudly.

As students continue to be announced and applauded, my entire thought process is hinged on the word *thankfulness*. I am thankful I trusted God through various seasons of doubt. I am thankful I did not buckle under pressure. I am thankful I moved here and survived my first semester as a private schooled student. I could not be more thankful to *live!* God has undoubtedly blessed me like I was promised: if I would only obey Him, sacrifice everything I had to be a light even when it was hard, and trusted Him through the process, there would be blessing. Look at me now!

"...and the winner of OEH's Outstanding Sophomore Character Award goes to Candice Gibbons." Principal Vanderbilt says into the microphone.

I am in shock.

"Go!" Claire pushes me out of my seat. Applause sweeps through the auditorium like the sound of rain on a tin roof. I am walking in utter dismay to the platform, not knowing what to do or how to react. *Another award?*

"Congratulations, Candice." Principal Vanderbilt whispers away from the microphone. Mrs. Lajuana gives me a thumbs up from the row of teachers standing behind Principal Vanderbilt. Coach Stanley even winks at me ever so slightly behind his wiry glasses.

"Thank you." I shake Principal Vanderbilt's hand as I am handed a framed certificate with my name printed in bold. Have I really won three awards in one semester? This all feels like a dream—something I could have never planned on my own. God has exceeded my dreams of being a leader at OEH. It is as if I am a legend here, but not by my own desire or actions. No, it was a subtle process. One where I yielded to God's will and stayed consistent through hard times. And now, I am reaping the benefits. Not only have I survived OEH, but I *conquered* it!

Chapter Fifteen

DECISIONS

F IVE SECONDS AGO, I was a private schooler. Now, the whimsical winds of Oklahoma are blowing my long brown hair in my lensed eyes, and I am finally free. I stepped outside as soon as the bell rang to breathe in the sun before cleaning out my locker. May's bright sunshine beams down on my body as I walk back inside. Today was my last day of school, and I would be lying if I said I was not sad. Right when it feels as if I am adjusting to the lifestyle of Oklahoma—the schoolwork, the people, the social cues—it is ending. And while I have no idea what summer holds, I do not think I will be roasting marshmallows at Carissa's bonfire. Nevertheless, I am happy and confident that everything's going to be okay. I am right with God.

"Bye Candice!"

"Have a great summer, Candice!"

"See you in the fall!" Voices call in the checkered-floored hallway I used to fear. Instead of walking with my head down and thoughts turned inward, I broaden my shoulders and wave at both freshmen, juniors, seniors, and yes, even my fellow sophomores. Everyone is happy and lighthearted, squealing at the final sound of this semester's bell and cleaning out their lockers. Coach Stanley has his music playing in the hallway so everyone can enjoy the tunes. Mrs. Lajuana has cookies set out beside her door shaped as cameras for all the

Journalism students. Even Mrs. Abernathy brought her baby and is waving to the students as they walk out of the door. OEH is like a family. No matter what kinds of students walk in and out of theses doors, everyone eventually finds their place. I have grown to love the high echoey ceilings, skylight beams of sunshine, checkered floors, and clanking lockers.

I could totally spend the rest of high school at OEH. I smile at the thought. What began as the worst semester of school evolved into a semester of spiritual growth, challenges, and healthy changes. Knowing I conquered running track, became a video sensation in Journalism class, and started breaking the sophomore clique problem makes me confident I can tackle anything else God throws my way. Yet, there is something scary. God had me here for a season. I regret to admit this twinge in my spirit concerning the future. No matter how hard I try to fight back bittersweet feelings, my time is up at this school. *Please, God! I can't be done! I am just now starting to fit in and like it here!* I try not to tear up as I simultaneously wave to students as they walk out of the double doors. *What if this is my last time to see them?*

It's time to go. God whispers inside. *You are called to something new.*

But what mission could be greater than moving to Oklahoma and being a light at OEH? Please God, give me a sign!

"Candice!" Mr. Groath calls out to me. This could be my sign. "I need to talk to you."

"Oh?"

"I may be tough on you in class, but I'm not blind to what kind of a girl you are…er, that is, how you've been such a light to OEH. All of the staff has been talking about you and the difference you made on your grade. That is no easy task. I am excited to see how God uses you here in the years to come. I believe you are going to be a leader even greater next year."

What in the world?!

"Wow, I, ugh…don't know what to say. That means a lot, Mr. Groath!" I grin uneasily. My stomach is doubling over with knots. I am so torn.

"You will be coming back here next year, right?" He studies my face.

"I hope so!" I smile hopefully.

"Well, good." He returns to his usual gruff voice. "Have a good summer, then." He pats me on the shoulder and turns on his heel.

"You, too!" I call out. And then I realize I am the only visible student remaining in the building. I see Dad's car waiting for me outside the doors. Whether I am coming back to OEH next year or not, it is once again time to say goodbye to a home I have grown to love.

Days have passed, but it might as well have been years. I never realized how attached I was to a building—the airbrushed faces, the girl-talk locker room conversations, even the hand sanitizer smell—I miss all of it. But if there is one thing I have learned over the course of this year, I should never base my decisions off my emotions. If I did, I would have never moved to Oklahoma in the first place. Nevertheless, it is extremely difficult to isolate my feelings from the decision to be at Oklahoma Excellence or not. My grandparents and friends support me on both sides, and Mom and Dad said the decision rests in my hands. *Argh!*

God, please give me a clear sign. I am reminded of my current situation—living in this rental house with my siblings. I have not been close to my siblings all semester due to school, so I should try to connect with them. *But how?* I am such a typical teen engulfed in my own problems. I have slowly, subtly abandoned the caring, compassionate girl I was in Missouri who was deeply involved with my family circle. It is like I do not even know *how* to connect with kids who are younger than me anymore, and I hate myself for it. Reluctantly, I fumble for my phone and begin what feels vaguely similar to a text I would receive from a cheerleader.

> *You're invited to a girl's sleepover in Candice and Kelly's room. Fun, food, and sister time! Movie begins at 8:00* <

I end the text with girly emojis. I can't remember the last time we all hung out together as sisters. Everyone feels like strangers. But as long as I can help it, I am not going to let out family slip into separation.

"Thanks for doing this!" Allison, the ever-blossoming pre-teen sisters with a new set of braces walks in the room Kelly and I share promptly at 7:59 p.m., carrying her pink blanket and two stuffed animals. "So, where's the popcorn?"

"The what? Oh, ugh…hold on." I have been looking up Bible verses on sibling unity ever since I came home. Time slipped away from me. I run into the kitchen and grab a bag out of the pantry—the same pantry I cried in and contemplated life. Glad that season is over. "Here!" I throw the bag into her arms.

"Yay!" Says a taller-looking Angel, wearing her same purple housecoat and scrunchy eye mask on her head. You're the best sister in the world." She says, finding a comfy spot on my bed to snuggle. My heart is set on having a heart-to-heart conversation with my sisters about what I have been going through, along with what God has been speaking to me about the blessings that are tied to obedience. I still feel like tonight is the least I could do after being an absent and depressed upon moving to Oklahoma. But it is never too late to turn things around, older sisters; it is never too late.

"And much more happened…but that's the overall storyline." I end after recounting a brief description of my semester at OEH.

Everyone has opened up about their own journeys of moving to Oklahoma. Allison shared about her feelings leaving her ballet class and friends in Missouri, but how God was helping her each day trust Him to bring her the right friend circle. Angel shared about her troubles as a public schooler, as well as the hurt behind missing our childhood cottage in Missouri. And then Bria, who walked in the room right when Angel finished, launched into her testimony.

"Honestly, I struggled with making friends this semester. Without all of my "BFFs" from Missouri, this semester has been horrible! Besides, I haven't had a school to go to like Candice and Kelly or a public school like Angel. And I never get to see them. You guys just go to school and come home and do homework like robots everyday…"

"*True,*" Kelly and I said simultaneously.

"And then there's Mom—obviously, we all know she's had a hard time moving. One day she told me to get out of the house and go buy my own groceries and live on the street!"

"*What?*" Everyone exclaimed.

"But I knew she was having a hard day," Bria laughed it off. "And I know she's still struggling, so we should all continue to pray for her."

"I agree." Said Kelly.

"I know all of us have been adjusting to a new church," Bria continued. "I mean, it's a really cool church, it's just different from our church in Missouri. But one night, our youth pastor came over and told me, 'Bria, you and I are going to change the world together.' And that really sparked something in me to stop seeing the world as, 'What can I get out of this?' to 'What can I *give* to the world?' So, there you go. There's my testimony." Bria ended in a happy voice.

"Wow, I had no idea. That is so cool!" I said in awe. I guess I never imagined God could work in two different people at the same time. *But of course, He can.*

"Overall, I had peace and excitement about God was doing." Kelly shared, but all of us could have guessed that much. Kelly has appeared to be an angel through this whole process, so that's why we were shocked to hear what she had to say next. "But I had strange physical problems at school. I fainted, had nosebleeds, and dealt with daily headaches. I felt like I needed to be stable when you, Mom, and Dad were out of control. But then when my body started blacking out with stress and everything, I was totally helpless. *I* felt out of control. At the end of the day, it all came down to where I was with God and whether I was relying on His strength."

"Oh, Kelly. I had no idea. I'm so sorry." I muttered, picturing her crying alone in an OEH bathroom while I was riding to lunch with the cheerleaders.

"It's okay," she said softly. "I am doing much better now. I think we all need to focus on helping Mom get through this."

"Yeah."

Everyone agreed. We closed our chat with a prayer before turning on our favorite movie, *Little Women.* As the movie rolls, I have this sudden realization there are many seasons in life—a time to grieve, a time to obey, a time to sacrifice, and a time to overcome—but the strongest time is one every person faces at one point or another: It is the time to trust, despite outward circumstances, feelings, or people. It is about learning to rely on the One who knows more than I will ever know. It comes from the deep sense of knowing that our lives are intricately connected with the spiritual world and that it is our duty and honor as humans to serve the One who created us. He is real. He is *for* us. And no matter what, He can be trusted.

Moving to Oklahoma *was* one big movie scene like I imagined. It was not solely the joy of flipping my hair and strutting down the checkered floor hallway as an influencer, nor was it merely the pain of crying in the pantry hoping God would change His mind and I could move back to Missouri. No, becoming an Oklahoman was determined by small, seemingly insignificant choices and moments of faith and trust. It started with the decision to step out and take a risk by attending a private school. Next, by choosing not to be fazed by those around me even when everything in me was failing—to sacrifice comfort, ease, and familiarity—but to stand up for my convictions and be there for others.

Track and field had the most significant effect on me during my depressing season; it taught me to *fight,* to work hard, and to keep running even when life gets hard. Physical activity literally boosts the brain. If I ever were to hit a hard season again, I would do just what I did this semester: run, because lessons I learned on the red track will stick with me through even greater challenges ahead. Coach Lakyn's motivation, Coach Stanley's humor, Mika's encouragement—these were all divinely purposeful. Just when I thought everything was over, things were only getting started. And I am certain the greatest change was inward. My level of trust and devotion to God has skyrocketed.

My identity is not tied to a state or a church or a school, but to God. With this perspective, I am the most fulfilled version of myself.

As I fall asleep, I listen to the familiar snores and heavy breathing. As strange as it sounds, I have missed their noises. We need each other. And we only have a few more years before princes come and steal us away one by one.

I glance over at the lonely cello I received for my sixteenth birthday, currently gathering dust in the corner of the room. Is it really for me, is it mine?

Images of the youth group leaders and students' faces from New Life Church fill my mind, and suddenly I feel I have missed being wholeheartedly involved at my new church.

Impulsively, I am reminded of my forgotten love of time to *think*.

God promised me blessings if I moved. I do not feel like that particular promise has been fulfilled. Even though OEH ended well with medals and memories, I believe that is only a glimpse of blessings to come. And that is what leaves me in suspense. Now that I feel I have left a mark on OEH, my heart is turned towards God's will, no matter what it may be. I think I know exactly where I am going to be for the rest of high school.

Goodbye, OEH.

Jeremiah 15:15-20 (NLT)

'Then I said,

"Lord, you know what's happening to me. Please step in and help me. Punish my persecutors! Please give me time; don't let me die young. It's for your sake that I am suffering.

When I discovered your words, I devoured them.

...I never joined the people in their merry feasts.

I sat alone because your hand was on me.

I was filled with indignation at their sins.

Why then does my suffering continue? Why is my wound so incurable?

Your help seems as uncertain as a seasonal brook, like a spring that has gone dry."

"This is how the Lord responds:

"If you return to me, I will restore you so you can continue to serve me.

If you speak good words rather than worthless ones, you will be my spokesman.

You must influence them; do not let them influence you!

They will fight against you like an attacking army, but I will make you as secure as a fortified wall of bronze.

They will not conquer you, for I am with you to protect and rescue you.

I, the Lord, have spoken!'

ACKNOWLEDGEMENTS

Melody Carlson, without reading your books *Harsh Pink, The Best Friend,* and *Prom Queen,* I might never have found my writing style. Thank you for representing the world of teen girls unashamedly. You truly sparked my career as a writer.

It is my honor to work alongside such an affable team of assertive creators at Trilogy Christian Publishing, and specifically with my project manager, Melissa Miller. From rounds of edits to marketing contracts, together we have published two books in a year. Hoorah!

A huge thank-you to my intelligent Irish twin, Kelly Grace, for combing through the manuscript as my first editor, and to Timothy Davis Esq., for his generous time reviewing drafts and, most importantly, giving invaluable advice on Carissa. Miss Carlyle is indebted to you.

OEH: I owe you all the memories. I am especially thankful for Mr. Nichols, Mrs. Coles, and Mrs. Emig, whose voices carried me through the semester. And to everyone who unconsented to be in this book, along with those who knew I was writing it and did not stop me, thank you, or, sorry.

Classmates of Mrs. Burk: you helped me name this book! Here is your acknowledgment.

Reagan Findley, thank you for letting me climb the creepy backstage stairs to your desk when I was in cover design despair, you are amazing!

Dancers at Dance Studio 150, you reminded me what pressure and thrill it is to be a teenager. Particular thanks to Kia Cheyenne for letting me sit backstage during a performance while I was writing the manuscript in June 2022. It proved exceptionally beneficial.

To my assertive coworkers: Stacy, Lauren, and Vanessa—thank you for your grace as I tirelessly tied the strings to two book manuscripts in a year. Our office would certainly not function without each of your administrative expertise's, and your quotes are hilarious.

To my esteemed colleagues in the Wolvercote Cohort: your critical feedback and sound writing advice have proved leaps and bounds in my intellectual growth. The warmest gratitude to my two key tutors at Oxford, Dr Ballam and Helen Jukes, for Zoom calls and Life Writing sagacity. I realize my learning has just begun.

I could not have written *A Time to Stand* without my family. Dad, thank you for graciously sponsoring me and making my dreams come true; Mom, thank you for your motherly love during spring break and for letting me publish your darkest season, leaving it as a cliffhanger—who lets someone do that about them? You are the best! Kelly, thank you for being my priestly anchor through OEH; Bria, thanks for not leaving home when Mom told you to leave—we all need your humor; Allison, thank you for fulfilling my dream to be a real dancer; Angel, you'll always be my favorite; and Jordan, you are the best editing partner in the world.

Most importantly, to the girl who just moved: I wrote this book for you. It isn't meant to be a feel-good, meaningless time waster on 'to cheer or not to cheer;' it is a true story of sacrifice. I am not trying to overemphasize its importance—it is only a measly memoir by a teen writer. But I hope its message is of some comfort that no matter how rough a start for you in your new town, at your new school, there is a reward for perseverance, for staying true to yourself and your convictions, and for standing strong when life changes. I may be older, but I am still the same sixteen-year-old girl in this book.

ABOUT THE AUTHOR

Candice Gibbons is the teen author of *A Time to Trust: One girl's journey through loss and change* (Trilogy, 2022). She is devoted to seeing teenage girls find their ideal life in Christ and she writes only to glorify God. Candice is currently studying for her Undergraduate Diploma in Creative Writing at the University of Oxford. To track Candice's current adventures, follow her on Instagram @author_candicegibbons and read her latest work at candicegibbons.com. Rest assured; a third book is in the wings.

CPSIA information can be obtained
at www.ICGtesting.com
Printed in the USA
LVHW030122060123
736525LV00002B/386